Keeping

C000179710

Garden Farming Series

Keeping Rabbits

Elisabeth Downing

PELHAM BOOKS

Animals are such agreeable friends – they ask no questions, they pass no criticisms . . .

George Eliot
1819–1880

636·9322
DOWN.

100712508

First published in Great Britain by
PELHAM BOOKS LTD
27 Wrights Lane
London W8 5TZ
First impression 1977
Second impression 1979
Paperback edition 1984
Laminated hard cover edition 1987

British Library Cataloguing in Publication Data

Downing, Elizabeth
    Keeping rabbits.—3rd ed.—(Garden
    farming series).
    1. Rabbits
    I. Title   II. Series
    636'.9322   SF453

ISBN 0–7207–1789–2

Printed in Great Britain by
Hollen Street Press Ltd, Slough

Contents

Acknowledgements

Grateful thanks are due to J. Crispin Clark BVMS, MRCVS who made time for valuable criticism and help in the chapter on health in the rabbitry.

I should like to thank Miss Meg Brown for suggesting some interesting rabbit recipes.

I'm indebted to Dulcie Asker for her expert interpretative and typing skills.

Finally, I thank my husband for the cover illustration, annotation of the figures and above all for his constant (im)patient help and encouragement.

Introduction

Meat can easily become one of the most expensive single items in the weekly housekeeping bill, and as such we are for ever being assailed by the press as to how we can stretch it to make it go further, utilise and generally spend hours of time in the preparation of the cheaper joints, or even go without and live on dandelion leaves and soya flour.

Why should we forego meat or only eat it but once a week because it is so expensive when we know that it is extremely pleasant to eat, and supplies the protein that we need for the growth and repair of our bodies? Admittedly we *can* survive on protein obtained from a wide variety of plants and vegetables, but certain animal proteins besides being very palatable supply all the essential amino acids in suitable proportions for human needs.

The gentle tractable rabbit can help us. An average rabbit of similar weight to a chicken can produce a third more actual meat than the bird. The flesh is denser in texture than the chicken and the meat-to-bone ratio is better; in addition the carcase produces white tender flesh with a very minimum of fat. The fat on the rabbit has a very low cholesterol level compared with the larger meat-producing animals.

In this book I hope to show the newcomer to domestic-rabbit production how to produce meat all the year round with the minimum outlay and possibly even a little pin money from the sale of surplus rabbits and pelts. The newcomer will obviously come up against many pitfalls but I hope to be able to provide some practical advice which will help to alleviate some of the beginner's problems.

Rabbits, like all domestic animals, require the highest level of management and continual care, but with a little organisation this can prove an absorbing and profitable pastime which can involve the whole family. With home-made housing and conventional pelleted food augmented by scraps from the kitchen in moderation, and possibly food grown especially for them in the garden, it will be possible to keep expenses to a minimum. If your interests lie in that direction, the meat production can be a profitable byproduct of showing the fancy breeds, or simply keeping the animals as pets.

Time spent deciding what is exactly required to be produced, planning the method of housing and the type of feeding suitable for the existing circumstances and, most importantly, who will be responsible for each actual job, will be repaid sooner rather than later. Arguments over who really *is* responsible for checking the water supply daily, for example, will be too late when it is found that poor old Smokey has a nest of dead babies caused primarily by the fact that she was without water for a day while being fed on dry hay and rabbit pellets. These decisions must be agreed upon before the enterprise starts.

Conversion Table

Metric and Imperial Equivalents

Imperial	Metric	Metric	Imperial
1 inch	2·54 cm	1 cm	0·39 in.
1 foot	30·48 cm	1 cm	0·033 ft
1 yard	0·91 m	1 m	1·094 yds
1 mile	1·61 km	1 km	0·62 miles
1 sq. yd	0·84 sq. m	1 sq. m	1·196 sq. yds
1 cu. yd	0·76 cu. m	1 cu. m	1·31 cu. yds
1 pint	0·57 litre	1 litre	1·76 pints
1 gal	0·0056 cu. m	1 cu. m	219·97 gals
1 gal	4·55 litre	1 litre	0·22 gals
1 fl oz	28·4 ml	1 ml	0·035 fl oz
1 oz	28·35 g	1 g	0·035 oz
1 lb	0·45 kg	1 kg	2·20 lb
1 acre	0·405 hectare	1 hectare	2·47 acres
$x\,°$F	$\frac{5}{9}(x-32)\,°$C	$y\,°$C	$(\frac{9}{5}y+32)\,°$F

Metric abbreviations

cm	centimetre
m	metre
km	kilometre
ml	millilitre
g	gram
kg	kilogram

1 Making a Start

The satisfaction gained from eating homegrown vegetables is becoming known to an increasing number of people. The improved flavour of the crisp, freshly harvested article over the commercially produced, much-travelled, pale and wilted one, is being appreciated more and more.

At first, home meat production might well be dismissed as impracticable, but in actual fact it is possible to produce a regular supply of rabbits for the table in less space than is needed to grow a few lettuce or radishes.

In the last twenty years, strains of a few especially meaty breeds have been developed to produce up to sixty or more young per doe yearly. These animals are kept in controlled-environment houses where high standards of management must be the rule. The capital outlay for this type of house is initially extremely high and feeding costs will also be a major expense of the enterprise.

Early in 1960 a body known as the Commercial Rabbit Association was formed under the sponsorship of the British Rabbit Council. This association was formed mainly to promote rabbit production on a commercial scale, to draw up and operate an accredited breeders scheme, to encourage research into rabbit production and promote the setting up of marketing facilities. Each year the Association organises courses of one or of three to four days' duration at various centres, generally local county schools or colleges of agriculture.

The family wishing to augment their own butcher's meat with homegrown rabbit may well benefit from attending such a course, but I feel that the breeding stock required for the small home enterprise is best obtained from a reputable breeder of one of the larger, meatier, conventional breeds. I do not intend to go into the finer points of the thirty or more breeds of rabbit for which the British Rabbit Council lays down standards; these can be obtained from the Council (see address, page 141).

Breeds of rabbits vary enormously in size from the tiny Polish or Netherland Dwarf which mature at a kilogram (or $2\frac{1}{4}$ lb) to the Flemish Giant and New Zealand White which mature at 5 kg or more (11 lb). Exponents of the different breeds extol their relative merits; some say the Rex breeds produce a fine-grained meat which is delicately flavoured, while others prefer the good meat carcase of the English rabbit, one of our oldest breeds. The good mothering qualities of this rabbit are renowned. Strains of New Zealand White, a large white-coated meaty rabbit, have been developed especially for the table to produce large litters of uniform quality as have other breeds, e.g. the Californian. There are also animals of these varieties which have not been so highly bred which may, I feel, suit the needs of the domestic producer better. The highly bred animal *may* possibly not stand up to the vagaries of family life in the back garden and could fail to come up to expectations. However, her less prolific cousin might well *enjoy* being a member of the family, prospering on a mixed diet of conventional rabbit pellets and also some garden and kitchen waste.

We must never forget that the good feeding and general management of our rabbits are going to have a profound effect on the end product. Where a potentially good animal is poorly housed and improperly fed, the result will be disappointing with small uneven litters showing slow growth rates. However, the less highly bred animal given ideal conditions will produce as well as she can. This does not mean to say that excellent management can improve the basic genetic makeup of the animal.

We must know something of the breeding of the stock we buy. Body weight and conformation are highly heritable whereas the milking ability of the doe and her litter size are very much influenced by her environment.

Table 1

Breeds Commonly used for Commercial Meat Production

Breed	Colour	Meat Quality	Average Weight
Californian	White with dark nose, ears, feet and tail	Fine texture good flavour	3·7 kg (8 lb)
New Zealand White	White Albino	Medium texture	4·5 kg (9 lb)

Other Breeds used for Meat Production

	Average Weight	
	kg	lb
Argente champagne	3·6	8
Beveren	3	7
Chinchilla giganta	4·5	10
Dutch	2·2	5
English	3	7
Fox	2·7	6
Flemish Giant	5	11
Havana	2·7	6
Lop	4 5	10

This list includes a few of the breeds which can be used for meat production. On joining the British Rabbit Council, full lists of recognised breeds and their exhibition standards can be obtained.

HYBRIDS Some commercial rabbit producers have developed hybrids from specially selected strains or breeds which produce high-quality, evenly sized stock. The production of hybrid breeding stock is best left to the specialist.

The phrase 'conformation of the animal' is frequently bandied about by livestock breeders and may not be clearly understood by the novice. Basically it covers the makeup and physical proportions of the animal. A good meat rabbit can consist of the maximum of meat with the minimum of bone. This is combined to form a blocky compact body. The bold head is wider in the male than the female and in both sexes leads to a short neck and broad shoulders. These are well set on to the back which is thickly muscled with meaty hindquarters. Generally the female will be longer in the back, to make room for plenty of young.

It is best to avoid the animal which is obviously very heavily boned and carries a large ungainly head. The long meagrely muscled back with undeveloped legs will yield little meat. However, the meat to bone ratio of a good animal should be in the region of 5 to 1.

The conformation of the rabbit is readily ascertained with a little practice, but stock must also be basically vigorous, healthy, bright eyed and alert. The flesh must appear firm and the coat shining. Features equally important but not so readily apparent must be the ability to produce large litters all the year round which grow fast with the minimum of food.

One feature often overlooked in the selection of stock is temperament. A friendly calm rabbit is far easier to manage. She is less likely to respond to any form of stress which may result in infertility, small uneven litters, poor growth rates and food-conversion ratios. Excitable animals may be found more often in the highly bred commercial strains. Amongst the forms of stress which our domestic animal may have to cope with can be the noise of children playing, dogs barking and the widely ranging temperatures experienced in the smaller domestic rabbitry. Unavoidable seasonal changes in diet where the food is mainly homegrown are inevitable and however slowly the change from one diet to another is made, the temperamental animal may resent it and be put off her food. In the controlled-environment unit where the day length and temperature are reasonably constant, where management is knowledgeable and highly skilled, and the rabbit fed *ad lib* with a standard pelleted feed, it *may* be possible to get good results from animals of a more excitable strain which also have the ability to produce many large, fast-growing litters each year.

The Secretary of the local Fur and Feather Club, whose address can often be obtained from the County Reference Library, may be more than helpful in the search for owners of breeding stock for sale. The Commercial Rabbit Association (address on page 141) has a register of accredited breeders. Stock records at the actual rabbitry are inspected by the Commercial Rabbit Association before being awarded accreditation. But it must always be remembered that strains within actual breeds vary enormously.

When buying breeding stock from either a large commercial concern or the domestic producer who keeps a few rabbits in the back garden, try to find out initially if the breeder is reputable. Be prepared to visit several rabbit keepers. The large breeder will have stock for sale from fully recorded sires and dams, with such information as weight, fertility, litter numbers per year, and food consumption. The stock from the larger breeders may already be vaccinated against certain rabbit diseases.

However, the smaller producer may also keep comprehensive records and any reputable breeder will be only too delighted to show these to a prospective buyer of his stock, but suspect the breeder with clean new record cards outside each pen! This does not mean to say that the small breeder who keeps few records is to be ignored. The rabbit keeper who has happy and contented, well-fed, meaty stock which obviously supply the family with meat pie on occasions is not to be overlooked. This type of stock will be well accustomed to life with a family. Some may even be prize winners at rabbit shows. The chance is, though, that this stock may not be so likely to produce a uniform litter of 2 kg (4½ lb) rabbits at eight weeks which is what one may expect to produce from stock from a reputable commercial rabbitry.

Having selected a few breeders to inspect make a note of the type of housing, feeding arrangements and type of food, when you visit. Check the temperament by noting how the individual rabbit responds to the sight of a stranger and to strange noises. The rabbitry where all the stock rushes to the corner of the pen must be suspect. They may be being incorrectly and irregularly fed, roughly handled or just excessively nervous. Make a point of noticing the size of groups in one cage; this may indicate the actual litter sizes unless two small litters are combined for fattening. Note the cleanliness of the hutches and especially the food and water containers, and don't be afraid to be guided by your nose! Of course the number of young with does, their obvious wellbeing and health can be a guide to their good management. An absence of lactating does with adequate-sized litters during the winter months is a sign that stock from this strain should be avoided. (Our meat supply must not be allowed to dry up, but if the animals are housed out of doors entirely this may be inevitable). Don't be tempted to buy stock through an advertisement, without enquiring carefully why the stock is available. Send a friend to see the stock if it is not possible to inspect personally and check on all available records. A glib reference to large litters must be backed up by records at least or obvious signs of plenty of young plump rabbits.

It is difficult to quote actual prices for breeding stock, but a look at the advertisement pages of *Fur and Feather*, a fortnightly journal concerning many small stock including rabbits, may give a fair idea of what is a reasonable price.

A breeding quartet of three does and a buck will form a relatively easily worked rabbitry. This will be capable of producing as much rabbit meat as an average family will possibly want with a surplus of fat or young stock (depending on your management and the capabilities of the stock) for sale to friends or for disposal at the local market or even to a butcher. It has been found that possibly the best age to buy breeding stock is about four months of age (before they have been mated), with the buck a month older than the doe. Some breeders will supply ready-mated does, but a journey or even a new environment can cause the animal to absorb the embryos or even to abort. Buying the younger stock ensures that they will have time to settle into their new surroundings before they have the added burden of pregnancy with which to cope.

The stock having been bought (ideally from one producer to cut down the risk of cross infection), they are now ready to be transported home. Where possible collect them personally; the duration of the journey and the resultant stress can thus be cut to a minimum. A strong cardboard box lined with straw (or hay) which is big enough to allow the individual animal to stretch but not to roll around and get bruised, will be suitable if holes are made in the lid. Don't condemn the creatures to a journey in the hot airless boot of a car. A more substantial wooden box can be bought from suppliers of rabbit sundries or can be quite simply made (see Figure 1). Avoid ventilation holes which will be draughty if the box is left unattended. Also avoid a glass or wire netting lid as this will afford little shelter from sun, rain or even other inquisitive animals.

Before the expected arrival check from the breeder the diet the rabbits have been fed. Where a pelleted ration is fed it is often possible to obtain the same make. If this is not possible, the breeder may be able to sell you up to three weeks' supply to feed in decreasing proportions with your own rabbit pellets (see page 49). Some domestic rabbits are fed a combination of oats, pellets, green stuff and roots. Find out what time of day they have been used to being fed. Check the type of water container and if it is not the same as yours make sure that the animal is drinking, that your drinkers can't be missed and that they are in a thoroughly accessible place.

This may all sound excessively fussy but some animals are extremely conservative and a day or two without food (or very little) will cause the rabbit to

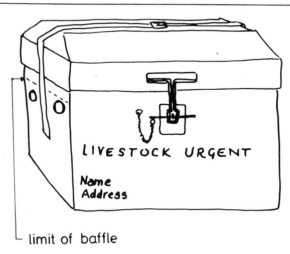

limit of baffle

Fig. 1 Travelling box. Note hasp fastening, buckled lid strap, ventilation holes with internal baffle to prevent draughts. The lid will be hinged.

lose condition rapidly, especially in hot or very cold weather.

As soon as the animals arrive, check their condition. A sweaty, damp rabbit may be incubating some illness or be just very upset by the journey. If the animal is obviously unfit, eyes gummy and half closed, nose excessively moist and condition generally poor, make a note of its ear-tag number (if any) and if there is a guarantee, return the stock as soon as possible. Also keep a sharp eye on any droppings; a healthy rabbit will pass firm pellets. In the unlikely event of an animal arriving dead, take it to a veterinary surgeon as soon as possible for a post-mortem and a signed statement of the rabbit's condition. Even if they were not guaranteed, a reputable breeder would replace the stock on being sent the relevant post-mortem information. When animals are sent in non-returnable boxes it is as well not to destroy these until the guarantee period, if any, expires.

When taking receipt of the initial stock they can be put directly into the previously prepared hutches. Any new breeding stock being brought in to replace or augment existing stock must be housed as far from the home stock as possible until it is known that they are fit and disease free: a period of about three weeks. The prepared hutches must have been well littered (except where wire cages are used), with fresh food, hay and water available and individual hutch records ready to complete.

Firmly and gently remove the animal from the box. Rabbits, like all animals, hate indecision on the part of their handlers and when insecurely held can scratch badly in the ensuing struggle. Rabbits handled in markets are unfortunately often either held by the ears alone or by the loose skin on the back. This is extremely dangerous to the rabbit possibly causing damage and bruising. The correct way can be seen in

Fig. 2 Lifting the rabbit. Weight taken by the left hand, right hand steadies the rabbit by its ears.

Figure 2, where the weight of the animal is taken on the hand and the ears are grasped with the other hand only to steady the animal. The experienced handler may hold young rabbits up to eight weeks of age or 2 kg (4 lb) or so in weight, by holding the animal across the loins. This requires practice, but an over-vigorous grasp can badly damage the animal internally. A child must be taught how to handle an animal very carefully, making sure that the rabbit is

Fig. 3 Safe way for a child to hold a rabbit.

initially not too heavy for him to carry (see Figure 3). Improperly held, the rabbit may scratch, which can cause the child to drop the animal. It is a good plan to supervise all handling by children initially and see that a table is ready to catch any unfortunate creature that may struggle.

The confident animal that knows its handler is far less likely to struggle. When a rabbit is put into a hutch it will often put its legs out and catch its claws on the floor or door. In order to avoid this, try putting it in backwards with its head towards you.

Leave the newcomers in peace for an hour or so and resist the temptation to rush out and peer in the hutches. If they have obviously not eaten by evening, try taking the food out and offering a little fresh food. There is nothing more off-putting than quantities of stale, uneaten food.

The next morning, whistle or talk as the rabbits are approached, noticing the smell of the shed if any. A sweet rabbity smell is in order, but stuffiness or strong ammonia fumes can indicate faulty ventilation or possibly impending disease. The good stockman will quickly notice an unhealthy atmosphere. Check that food and water have been taken (see page 116), notice the type of droppings (see page 115), clean and refill the water pots and feed containers if necessary. Pay attention to the general demeanour of the rabbits. The animal which has settled will hold its ears upright, moving them with interest, its eyes will be bright and its nose constantly twitching. Talk gently all the time and they will soon learn to associate the voice with food and comfort. Depending upon the temperament of the animals, avoid too much handling until they appear to be thoroughly at home.

Housing

The newcomer to rabbit keeping may well be tempted into thinking that female rabbits kept in an old tea chest with periodic visits to the buck down the road will supply his family's needs for meat. He may also be misled into imagining that little Johnnie and his sister will be kept out of mischief gathering weeds for the rabbits augmented by limp cabbages cadged from the local greengrocer. Father meanwhile is des-

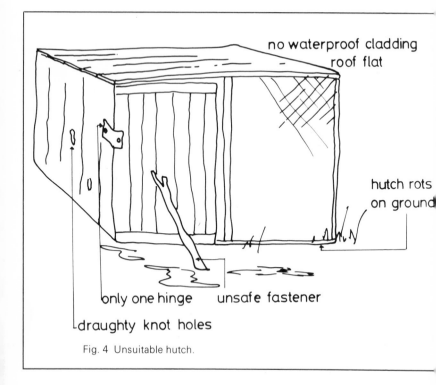

no waterproof cladding
roof flat

hutch rots on ground

only one hinge   unsafe fastener

draughty knot holes

Fig. 4 Unsuitable hutch.

perately knocking up more hutches for the rapidly increasing rabbit population. This lack of fore-thought can be extremely expensive in time and money and, more importantly, the animal's health.

There are many ways of adequately housing rabbits and each serves a purpose in differing circumstances. Obviously the commercial rabbit producer who sends all his fat rabbits to a packing station will find it easier to invest a fair amount of money on purpose-built sheds. Plans for such a unit need to be submitted to the local District Council to see if planning permission is needed. If permission is not required, building may commence, not forgetting that certain building regulations may have to be adhered to. If, on the other hand, permission is required, apply to the District Council for planning permission. If this is refused an appeal can be made; this may take six months or longer to be heard.

Smaller outdoor hutches containing half a dozen or so does, or a shed suitable to house them, will not normally require planning permission; but it is just as well to enquire from the local District Council before you *do* start the enterprise. Normally a unit supplying *household* quantities of rabbits will not require permission.

The Allotments Act of 1950 states that no landlord, including a Public Corporation, can prevent a person keeping rabbits if he has suitable accommodation and the animals do not cause a nuisance. In fact if the stock are kept in a reasonable manner, a landlord cannot forbid his tenants keeping rabbits in domestic quantities. However, whether you are the owner of your land or a tenant, careful consideration for your neighbours will have to be exercised.

In a commercial unit where a certain amount or even all of the feeding, watering and cleaning is done mechanically, one person may be expected to look after two hundred or more does depending on the layout of the farm. On a smaller scale it can take up to two hours daily to look after ten female rabbits and their young, and the three or so does and one buck which will supply the needs of most families will take even less time.

A family keen on showing fancy breeds may well own a larger number of rabbits than the concern which will merely provide meat for the family. The reject show animals will often take longer to reach killing age than a rabbit bred specially for meat production, therefore space must be provided to allow for a greater number of hutches.

Site

When deciding on a suitable area for the rabbitry, the possibility of expansion must always be borne in mind when planning the original layout. A sheltered spot out of the prevailing wind is ideal, with a south-facing sunny aspect where shade can be available.

The type of soil will not be so vitally important to our family unit as it would be to a large commercial farm with its severe drainage problems. Obviously a sandy soil will mean that even in the wettest weather the area around the rabbitry will not become too muddy, but should the soil be heavy, suitable consideration must be paid to the possibility of laying gravel or even concrete paths around the hutch area.

Within reason, the animals need to be housed near enough to human habitation to make casual visits during the day the rule rather than the exception. All livestock thrives on quiet and frequent visits. Even the most shy and temperamental doe will become more tame in time and consequently more likely to rear better and larger litters.

Methods of housing

Wild rabbits spend much of their time, when they are not eating, in a warren. This consists of a series of inter-connecting burrows in a bank or amongst undergrowth. The pregnant doe, however, digs a short burrow of about a yard long in which she makes her nest and rears her young. From this, we learn that the rabbit likes warmth and cover and individual provision for a nursing doe.

Whatever method of housing is employed, the domestic rabbit needs cover and protection from the elements and obviously room to eat, sleep and move about, with ample light and ventilation. The pregnant and nursing doe will need individual housing.

Rabbits can be housed in:

1. Individual wooden, outdoor hutches;
2. Tiered, outdoor wooden hutches with lean-to roof and 90 cm (3 ft) overhang;
3. Outdoor apex-type mobile runs;
4. A wooden shed containing hutches.

These methods of housing or combinations of two or more will be reasonably cheap to make and easy to run. Wire cages made from Twilweld or other metal which need to be housed in controlled-environment sheds will prove extremely expensive and need a high level of management for satisfactory results.

On the small domestic scale *outdoor hutches*, provided that they are adequately roofed against the elements, sheltered from the wind and have shading in the summer against the sun, will prove satisfactory. They do, however, make feeding and cleaning-out a major operation if it is snowing or raining. Temperature control is difficult and the extra lighting needed to facilitate winter breeding may be inconvenient to provide in the darker months.

It may be worth spending a little extra time either housing the hutches in a lean-to-type shed or, in the case of tiered hutches, erecting a single span roof which overhangs the building by 90 cm (3 ft), affording shelter to the attendant as well as added protection from the elements for the animals.

A *double- or single-span shed* can afford a far greater control over the environment. But care will have to be taken over ventilation to avoid the build-up of disease. Adequate lighting, both natural (by way of windows) and artificial, will be needed. Finally, the house should be large enough to contain sufficient hutches. Wire doors to allow cleaning apparatus, wheelbarrows and crates easy access, are essential for ease of working.

Rabbits can be kept in *mobile runs* which incorporate sleeping accommodation and these can be

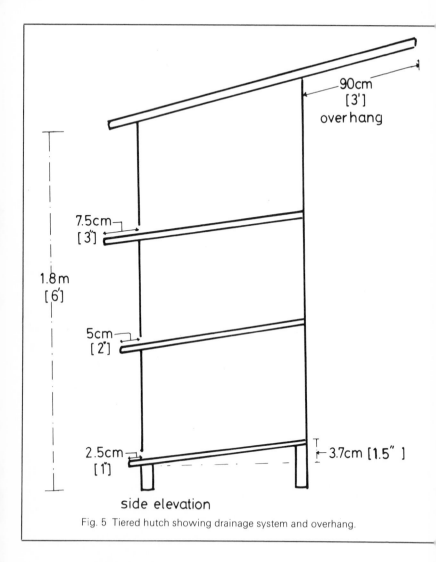

90cm [3'] over hang

7.5cm [3"]

1.8m [6']

5cm [2"]

2.5cm [1"]

3.7cm [1.5"]

side elevation

Fig. 5 Tiered hutch showing drainage system and overhang.

moved regularly over the lawn during the months of grass growth. This method can considerably reduce feeding costs as well as keeping the grass clipped.

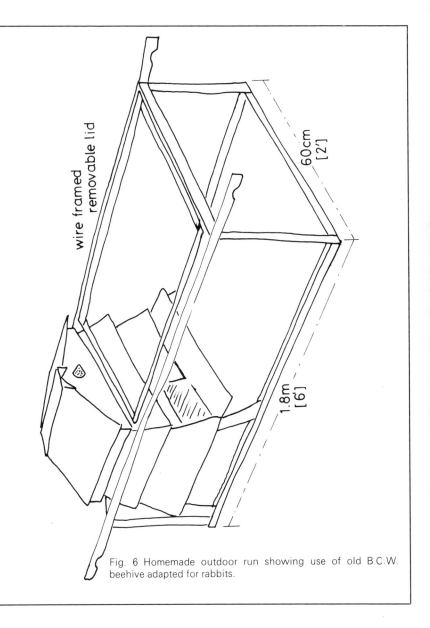

wire framed
removable lid

60cm
[2']

1.8m
[6']

Fig. 6 Homemade outdoor run showing use of old B.C.W.
beehive adapted for rabbits.

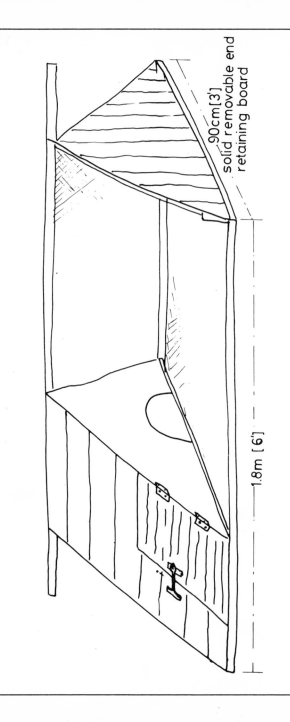

90cm [3'] solid removable end retaining board

1.8m [6']

Fig. 7 Apex Morant run.

Weaned rabbits can be fattened under this system, though I have even kept breeding rabbits in this way. Obviously in the colder, wetter parts of the country it may not be suitable in the winter.

I have seen rabbits kept in artificial warrens known as *colonies*. The animals can be kept out at grass in wired-in areas with small wooden shelters. But the problems of predators such as crows, foxes, cats and dogs loom large on the horizon. The fencing requires to be buried at least 30 cm (1 ft) to prevent stock burrowing out. The animals become extremely wild, there is difficulty over control of disease, records are virtually impossible to keep and, unless the bucks are removed soon enough, the young does become pregnant too early. A development of this is the colony pen which, taking up to thirty young rabbits, can be erected under cover with a wire-mesh floor. This must be adequately supported to take the final weight of the fattening rabbits.

To sum up, the housing needs of the rabbit and the number of hutches required must initially be ascertained allowing for a few extra for resting (see page 137) and emergencies. The hutches must provide sufficient room for the animals and a strong, safe, dry, easily cleaned hutch with easy access for the attendant to ensure adequate attention.

Dogs and cats may frighten the stock on occasions especially if strange animals gain access. A shed with a wire door as well as a solid wooden one will help here. It may be necessary to erect chainlink fencing around the rabbitry. This will deter predators and keep out unwanted visitors.

Size of hutch

Obviously the larger breeds will require more room than the smaller ones. If we take the figure of 930 sq. cm (1 sq. ft) of space to each 450 g (1 lb) weight of the adult animal, we will find that the average 3·6 kg (8 lb) rabbit will be happy in a hutch 120 cm long by 60 cm wide by 60 cm high (4 ft long by 2 ft wide by 2 ft high) in which to rear her family until weaning.

The young weaner rabbits will each enjoy 1850 sq. cm, (2 sq. ft) floor space, so that a suitable hutch for a litter of rabbits to killing weight of 2 kg (4½ lb) would be 1·8 metres long by 75 cm wide by 60 cm high (6 ft long by 2 ft 6 in. wide by 2 ft high). The individual hutch for the stud buck needs to be ample to allow room for the visit of the doe at mating time, perhaps 1·05 m long (3½ ft) by 60 cm wide (2 ft), depending on the size of the buck.

Roofing

Whatever the housing, roofing must be weatherproof with an adequate slope and overhang to drain water away. It must also be anchored securely against wind and rain. The life of the roof covering will depend on proper maintenance, the exposure of the building, local weather conditions and the material used.

Corrugated iron. This is noisy, draughty, ugly, hot in sunny weather and cold in winter. Condensation becomes a problem in rapidly changing temperature conditions. It needs yearly tarring for durability. It is still only available in Imperial measurements 8 ft by 3 ft.

Corrugated Asbestos. This is far more expensive and very brittle to work. All holes will have to be bored before it is fixed, to avoid cracking. Secure the sheets with screws and washers or a screw nail which will screw itself when nailed in. It can be sawn using water as a lubricant. The advantage of this material is that it does not need any maintenance.

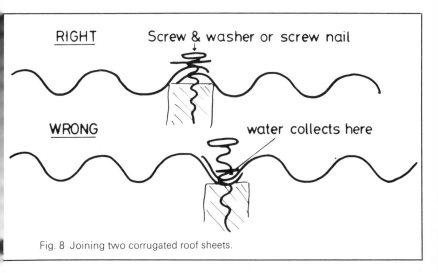

Fig. 8 Joining two corrugated roof sheets.

Rubberoid Felt. This can be purchased in 1-, 2- or 3-ply rolls 10 metres long and 1 metre wide. Its life depends on the care taken when it is laid. Ideally work it in summer to facilitate rolling it out without cracking or tearing. When sections are overlapped allow a 5 cm (2 in.) lap. It can be laid either down the roof or along. Builder's laths will be needed every 180 cm (6 ft) not necessarily at the edges of the felt, and laid vertically so that the rain does not accumulate. When cutting felt use a knife dipped in water or tin snips. Fasten the felt with $\frac{5}{8}$ in. clout-headed galvanised nails every 5 cm (2 in.). When covering large areas see that the first sheet is laid absolutely square for obvious reasons. It is essential to repair tears immediately they occur with mastic or patches burnt on carefully with a blow lamp. As the felt ages, its life is prolonged by yearly tarring. Mineralised felt is more expensive but will last longer.

Other suitable materials for roofing are marine-quality plyboard, and external-quality hardwood.

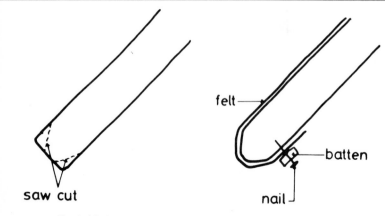

felt

batten

saw cut

nail

Fig. 9 Method of attaching roofing felt.

Windows

Past experience has shown that the maximum possible adequate natural light is preferable to a solely artificial light. In individual or tiered outdoor hutches it is generally found suitable to have at least half one side of the hut open to the light with wire netting over the aperture. Windows in a shed will need to both assist ventilation and to illuminate. Hopper-type glazed windows opening inwards can be used to control the ventilation. Attention must be paid to keeping the windows regularly cleaned to allow maximum daylight. The provision of sacking or even shutters for extreme weather conditions, e.g. cold winds or extremely sunny weather, will help to maintain an equable temperature. The siting of the windows must avoid directing strong sunlight into the hutches.

Doors

The door to the rabbit shed will need to be wide

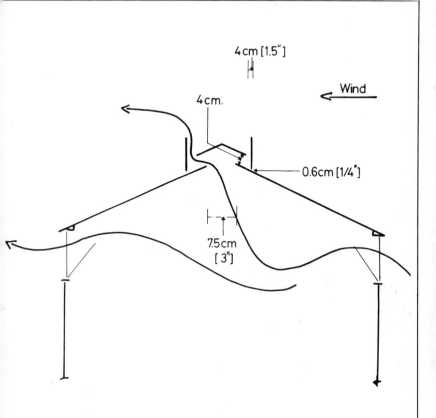

4 cm [1.5"]

4 cm.

Wind

0.6 cm [1/4"]

7.5 cm [3"]

Fig. 10 Ventilation by means of hopper windows and conventional V-type ridge cap with side protection to prevent downdraughts.

enough to allow a loaded barrow, a rabbit crate or bales of hay and straw to be taken through. The fasteners need to be easily manipulated by humans but out of the reach of animals. This applies to both

33

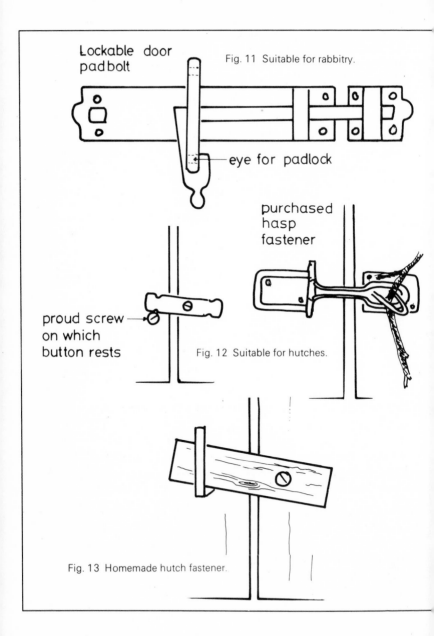

Lockable door padbolt

Fig. 11 Suitable for rabbitry.

eye for padlock

purchased hasp fastener

proud screw on which button rests

Fig. 12 Suitable for hutches.

Fig. 13 Homemade hutch fastener.

sheds and hutches. A padlock may be found necessary for the shed door. A door made of framed 1 in. wire netting inside the solid shed door may be found essential to keep the shed cool in summer and at the same time keeping unwanted visitors out.

When constructing tiered hutches a single door will suffice for all the hutches provided that a removable retaining board 15 cm (6 in.) high is incorporated to restrain the animals when the communal door is opened.

Floors

Though the faecal material voided by rabbits is passed in a hard dry pelleted form, there is also a certain amount of urine. If allowed to accumulate, the latter will quickly soak any litter and also assist the possible transmission of disease.

Solid Floors. The solid floor of either the hutch or shed needs primarily to be impervious to vermin and easily cleaned. Ideally the floor of the rabbitry will be made from non-absorbent, non-slippery material which is both dry and long lasting.

Concrete which has been tamped will be ideal but is costly and impractical for actual hutches. In the hutch, wooden floors made from timber 1·25 or 1·5 cm (about $\frac{5}{8}$ in. thick) will be suitable, with a small gap between the boards to assist drainage and to allow expansion of the timber when wet.

Wire Floors. The wire cage often employed on a commercial unit has little to commend it to the domestic meat producer. The wire floor, though making cleaning out a matter of removing the faecal matter from beneath the hutch, can lead to draughts and chilled rabbits in any but a completely controlled-environment house. Sore hocks can become a

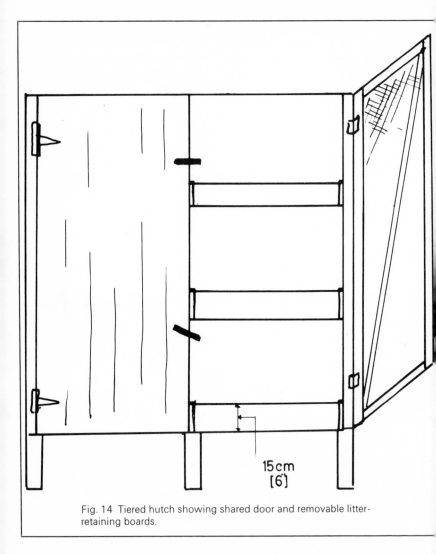

Fig. 14 Tiered hutch showing shared door and removable litter-retaining boards.

problem, especially in rabbits of Rex breeding (see page 127). If wire *must* be used no wire netting should be involved, but use a wire mesh which is galvanised after manufacture. This will need to be 12 gauge with mesh 19 × 19 millimetres.

Ventilation

Insufficient ventilation is easily detected on entering the rabbit shed by a strong smell of ammonia and with condensation apparent on the ceiling of the building. This problem will not arise so frequently in individual or tiered outdoor hutches. Each rabbit gives off heat and water vapour when it breathes which will need to be removed without a draught being created. Fresh air must be continually introduced to the animals. Working on the principle that warm air rises, it is wise to have the inlets at floor level and the outlets high up. The aim is to produce a house where there are no detectable draughts and a warm animal smell is apparent, without any trace of ammonia.

Where only a few animals are housed, it may be possible to rely on the fresh air which enters the door being drawn up and out of the opposite window. The hutches will need to be placed away from the wall to avoid draughts and to allow the air to circulate.

Ideally the ventilation should be controlled to maintain an even temperature. Simple adjustable inlets and outlets are easily constructed. Porous bricks or grilles can be let in at floor level or baffled inlets constructed to cut down the risk of draughts. Outlets can consist of a ridge opening on the roof which might be adjustable, cowls or even adjustable windows high up in the wall. The aim should be 6·5 sq. cm (1 sq. in.) of inlet per rabbit and a little more at the outlet. Obviously the outlets and inlets will have to be periodically checked to see that they are not blocked.

Adjustment of the ventilation will require practice in order to maintain a draught-free, sweet-smelling, pleasant atmosphere. Stuffy, humid air conditions will assist the development of airborne bacteria and contribute to the spread of virus diseases.

Feeding equipment

Troughs and drinkers must be made of easily cleaned materials to cut down the risk of disease build-up. They also need to be easily filled, accessible to the rabbit, waste-free, stable and cheap. There must be adequate feed space available for all the animals in one hutch to feed at one time or a very uneven litter may result. Allow up to 7 cm trough space (3 in.) per rabbit for single-sided hoppers; for double-sided, allow 3·5 cm.

Drinkers—Contrary to popular belief, rabbits need a constant water supply for optimum health and growth. 0·68 kg (1½ lb) of green stuff or roots daily may supply up to 0·6 litres (1 pint) of moisture which would maintain a medium-sized adult. A lactating doe, however, would need considerably more moisture as will growing young, especially in hot weather. Thus, for the animal's comfort and health, a constant supply of clean, fresh water must be maintained.

Drink containers must be easy to clean thoroughly, readily accessible to humans and animals, and difficult for the animal to upset. Where few animals are kept, glazed earthenware pots about 10 cm (4 in.) across and 5 cm (2 in.) deep and sufficiently heavy to avoid upset can be obtained from pet shops. Unfortunately rabbits often use them as urinals and once this habit has developed it is almost impossible to eradicate. Galvanised half-moon drinkers which can be attached to the wall of the hutch or inside the wire are less likely to be tipped up and the height at which they are suspended can be adjusted to the size of the rabbit.

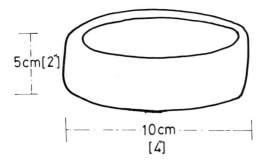

5cm[2"]

|— — — — 10cm — — — — —|
[4]

Fig. 15. Purchased earthenware pot suitable for food or water.

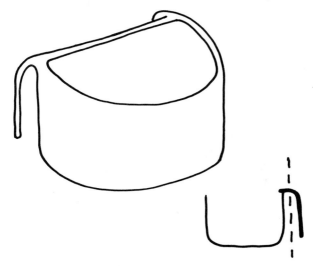

Fig. 16 Half-moon galvanised trough suitable for water or food.

Semi-automatic drinkers can be made from inverted
pint bottles attached to the outside of the cage with a
rubber bung in the neck through which 0·6 cm ($\frac{1}{4}$ in.)
glass tube protrudes. The end of the tube is rounded
and smoothed by a very hot flame. The animal then

39

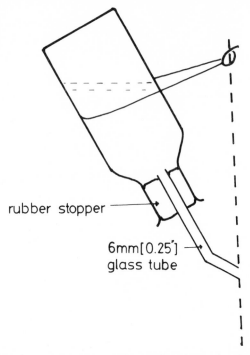

rubber stopper

6mm[0.25"] glass tube

Fig. 17 Water drinker. These can be purchased or made at home.

sucks the water as required. The bottle must be refilled daily with fresh water and frequently rinsed out with a bottle brush, warm water and detergent.

Feed Containers. Earthenware pots can be used for pelleted food as well as other dry foods. Those sold in pet shops for cats are ideal. Feeders can also be made from the harder woods as they are easier to keep clean and sweet. I have made them from oak obtainable from old chests of drawers. These are very stable and can be made as long as is required.

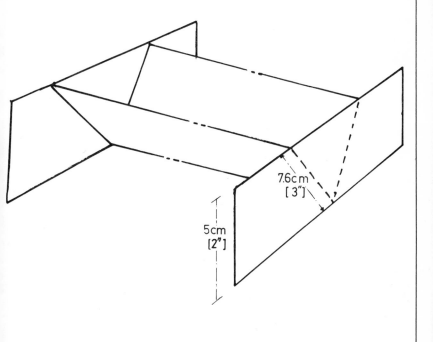

7.6cm
[3"]

5cm
[2"]

Fig. 18 Wooden hopper suitable for pellets and cereals.

Pellets are sometimes unavoidably dusty and rabbits do not readily wade through the dust to get to the pellets. A self-dusting hopper trough which can be hung outside the hutch and therefore easily refilled (the aperture for feeding being on the inside of the hutch) is quite easily constructed. However, this is only suitable for pellet feeding.

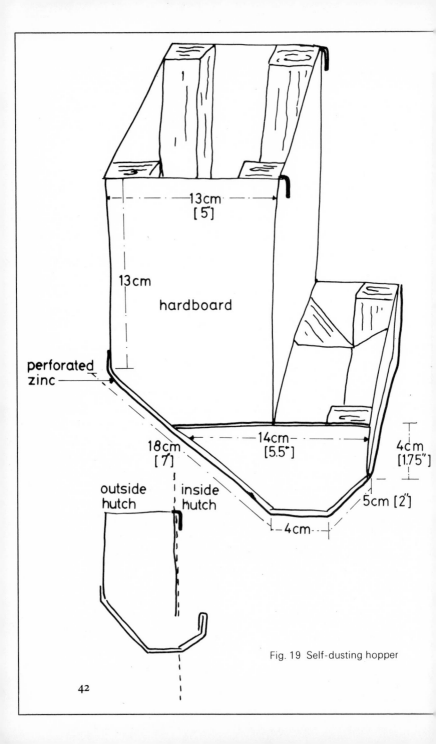

13cm
[5"]

13cm

hardboard

perforated
zinc

14cm
[5.5"]

4cm
[1.75"]

18cm
[7"]

5cm [2"]

4cm

outside
hutch

inside
hutch

Fig. 19 Self-dusting hopper

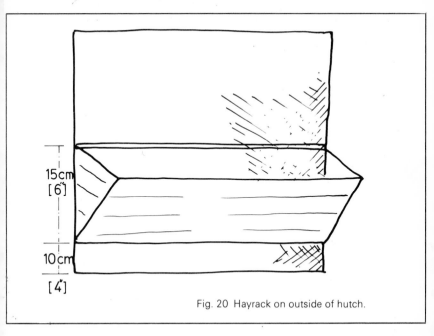

15cm
[6ʺ]

10cm
[4ʺ]

Fig. 20 Hayrack on outside of hutch.

Hayracks. Racks suitable for hay and green stuff are essential as food left on the floor of the hutch is easily fouled and therefore wasted. 2·5 cm ($1\frac{1}{3}$ in.) mesh wire is suitable here. It can be attached to the outside of the hutch to make for easier replenishment while the rabbits eat food through the wire of the door. This rack will need to be high enough to keep food off the floor and low enough for it to be reached without the rabbit standing upright on its hind legs, in fact easily accessible. The advantage of an outside rack is that there are no sharp or protruding parts on which the animal can catch or wound itself.

Handling tables

An old table is a useful extra. Scales can be stood on it while completing routine weighing. It will be used for standing animals on while they are being inspected or handled for any reason. A piece of sacking may be laid over the top to give a non-slippery surface and this can be renewed as necessary. The table should be as high as the handler requires; some people like to stand and others to sit whilst working.

3 Feeding

Anyone who lives near a wasteland area, common, or woodland will have noticed that wild rabbits are only too delighted to augment their diet of wild grasses and weeds with plants which have been tenderly nurtured in nearby gardens. From lettuces to lilies, bedding plants to beetroot, all will fall prey to the rabbit's destructive nibbling teeth. Not content with this, their habit is to take a choice piece from each plant, preferably the heart.

We *can* feed our rabbits on certain wild plants found growing on wasteland, around the hedges, and also the leaves of some vegetables which are grown for the kitchen. But to entirely feed the young from one or even two does in this way may involve tramping miles armed with a sack, and this is clearly not feasible unless one has little else to do. During the winter the supply of wild, edible feed is considerably reduced, the extent depending on the severity of the weather.

During the 1939–45 war, bona fide rabbit keepers registered with the Ministry of Agriculture Rationing Division, obtained 7 lb of bran per doe every three months. This was often fed as a wet mash in conjunction with boiled potatoes augmented by roots and hay in winter and weeds in the summer. It kept many families in the relative luxury of daily meat, as rabbit did not come under the meat-rationing schemes.

Since then, and particularly since the 1950s, rabbit farming on a commercial scale has been revolutionised by the advent of rabbit pellets. It has been found that a single standard ration can be fed to all ages and classes of stock thus avoiding the changeover problem of resistance to new food and the consequent stress which can lead to slower growth rates and possibly even disease. On a commercial scale this can be the difference between profit and loss.

The rabbit requires food consisting of edible carbohydrates, proteins, fibre, vitamins, minerals and water. These are needed in varying proportions for movement, growth and reproduction. The rabbit is basically a bulk feeder and, provided that these requirements are met and nutrients supplied in the correct proportions, it will thrive. These are normally found in a reputable pelleted ration or in sufficient quantities of green plants and roots, both wild and cultivated, in conjunction with hay and possibly straight cereals.

Principles of feeding

Regularity. All livestock likes to be attended to and fed regularly. The rabbit is no exception. Animals seem to have an inbuilt clock and if fed at certain times each day they thrive on this treatment. Try to plan feeding times to fit in with both the human family and the rabbit clock. Ideally some time around seven in the morning and just before dusk is suitable. Irregularity often causes gorging especially where green stuff is used and this can lead to stomach upsets and consequent possible disease. When a solely pelleted ration is fed *ad lib*, regular feeding is not so vital as long as they have food before them all the time, but they still *appreciate* regular times for attention.

Hygiene. No animal likes soiled foods. Food pots need to be regularly rinsed, then scrubbed thoroughly and scalded, as do the water containers. Green food fed on the floor is quickly soiled and this becomes unpalatable. Try to feed hay and green stuffs in a rack. If it must be left on the floor remember to place it at the furthest point away from the dunging area. Always remember to clear away any green feed or roots left from previous meals. Stale leavings may easily put some rabbits off their food. Pellets fed in a dish or trough must be finished before adding more; old pellets left underneath soon render the fresh pellets unpalatable. A self-dusting trough refilled from the top ensures that the pellets are not dusty (the dusty crumbs drop out at the bottom) and fresh pellets are always there to replace those eaten.

Use a clean container for collecting wild fodder. A clean hemp sack is good but if dragged along wet ground soon becomes dirty and may spoil the food already inside. Avoid gathering weeds from roadsides which dogs are known to frequent as these will be unattractive and possibly contaminated. Watch out for sprays which may have blown over from the farmer's field onto the road verges, these may poison the animals. Luckily many councils have now stopped using chemicals to control the herbage on the roadside and confine their tidying to cutters used after the herbage has flowered and seeded. Lately it has been found that the herbage growing on the verges of roads carrying heavy traffic may contain toxic levels of lead, so it is safer to confine one's activities to gathering herbage from the sides of the lesser-used roads and wastelands.

Quality. The dictionary describes quality amongst other things as the degree or grade of excellence. Quality of food can be judged by the experienced touch, eye and nose of the feeder, and of course by the rabbits' response to the particular food. High-quality feeding stuffs are particularly relished normally. Rabbit pellets should be pleasant smelling and with no trace of mustiness or dust which may cause respiratory trouble. Of the grains, oats should be plump, heavy and glossy. A thin, dull, light chaffy sample is best not fed. Maize is generally fed in a standard form of rolled and partially cooked flakes. Watch out for stale stock by testing it for dustiness or mustiness. Barley is generally fed crushed lightly and a good sample would show grains which will, though partially flattened, have obviously originally been large and full. A poor sample will have a proportion of grain too thin to roll. A desirable sample of bran will consist of largish flakes which will yield a fine dusting of flour adhering to the hand when it is run through the sample.

Don't ever be afraid to ask to open, see, feel and smell a sample of feed-stuff. This is one of the advantages of a personal visit to the mill for purchase. It is also cheaper to collect from a mill if at all possible when one is passing, as more favourable prices are available to the personal shopper. Try to develop a nose and feel for good grains and pellets. The rabbit will thrive on your good judgment. This ability to discern the good samples will develop with constant practice. A reputable miller will guard his reputation by supplying an appetising pellet or straight grain (e.g. oats, barley, bran), which is of good quality.

Good-quality hay is hard to obtain most years and is expensive. The newcomer will find it best to get expert advice when buying hay. A good-quality hay can be judged by thrusting a hand into the centre of a bale and pulling out a handful. There should be no hint of dustiness and the hay must not be obviously brittle. A suggestion of green will indicate that it was

47

saved in good condition, (i.e. not rained upon before being baled.) There should be plenty of leaf apparent as this is where the protein is found mainly. When bitten the stem of grass should taste wheaty and sweet. A dusty, musty sample with a strong aroma of tobacco is best avoided as it may cause bronchial infections and is not palatable. Hints on making hay at home will be found on page 62.

Slow Changes. When a pelleted ration is fed to rabbits throughout their lives, gross feed changes will not occur except when the young start to eat solid food while still suckling from their mother. However, changes in feeding will obviously occur during transition from one season to another when wild and homegrown foods are used, but the possible stress this causes can be ameliorated by easing the rabbits from one feed to another over a period of ten days or so if this is at all possible.

Table 2

Sample food costs/ton with equivalent costs/pound and /kg

£/ton	pence/lb	pence/kg
10	0·45	0·99
20	0·9	1·98
30	1·35	2·97
40	1·8	3·96
50	2·25	4·95
60	2·7	5·94
70	3·15	6·93
80	3·6	7·92
90	4·05	8·91
100	4·50	9·90

Bearing in mind that a varied succulent diet is always available, the actual change for example from carrots to mangolds (these cannot be fed until after Christmas as they may cause colic) can be made by introducing a small quantity of sliced mangolds whilst still feeding the carrots. The proportion of carrots will then be gradually reduced until none is fed after a week or ten days. Rabbits which have been accustomed to a wide variety of foods will be less likely to cut down the food intake if sudden changes are made in their ration. The greedy rabbit is also less likely to gorge.

Methods of feeding

Intensive Method. There are numerous methods of feeding rabbits and no hard and fast rule can be advocated for any particular situation. The commercial rabbit farmer obviously has not the time to gather wild foods or even feed homegrown greenstuffs, and in this situation a standard rabbit pellet is fed to all stock. This pellet must be of suitable size; a cylinder about 4 mm in diameter and 10 mm in length is commonly used. It must be sufficiently hard to prevent it breaking during storage and yet be palatable to the rabbit. The suggested storage life of the ration will normally be indicated on the bag. These pellets contain all the nutrients needed for rabbit growth and maintenance. Most compounders also include a preventive-level coccidiostat (see page 118) and this is also indicated on the label of the bag. Some compounders only manufacture a compound pelleted ration *without* medication against coccidiosis by special request. They may be loth to do this in quantities under 1 tonne. The label will state oil, protein and fibre content. The average contents will be approximately 3 per cent oil, 16·5 per cent protein and 12 per cent to 15 per cent fibre. Most rations come in the lower fibre content of 12 per cent in order that the pellets may be fed with a good-quality hay. This will give the rabbit something to do and helps fulfil the need for a bulky diet.

A rack is suitable for holding the hay (see page 43). In the case of wire cages it can be placed on the top, the rabbit reaching up and pulling it through the wire roof.

Cereals ('straights'). Cereals can be used for feeding rabbits but may well be rather low in protein, minerals and vitamins. However, *lightly* crushed oats can be suitable if fed as part of a ration. If crushed too much the rabbits will consume the grain and leave a lot of the husk which is expensive and wasteful. Wheat is seldom used whole as rabbits do not find it very palatable, and fed ground it is inclined to stick to the teeth in an uncomfortable paste. Maize is generally fed as a semi-cooked dry flake. This is low in fibre but high in carbohydrate. It is best not fed to fatteners as it is inclined to produce a soft fat which may be yellow (see page 87). Bran has always been the traditional rabbit ration. It is the husk of the wheat and is a byproduct of wheat ground for flour. Nowadays with modern milling processes, little flour is left on the bran so that its energy value is far less than bran produced as a byproduct of stone-ground flour. Pea and bean meal are seldom available in the small quantities wanted by the domestic producer, but they are a valuable source of vegetable protein. Rabbits fed these cereals alone would not produce such fast growth rates as those on a miller's compounded pellet. Animal proteins such as meat and bone meal and white fish meal are unpalatable to feed on their own and possibly dangerous. These animal protein meals form up to 10 per cent of a compounded pellet. They are inconvenient to handle at home, as unless they are mixed extremely well with the other cereals they are not consumed by the rabbit and are thus wasted.

Extensive Method—Homegrown Food. Most root vegetables grown in the garden are suitable for rabbit feeding, and in many cases both the root and the green top (e.g. carrot leaves) are particularly palatable. However, the leaf of the potato is poisonous while the green tops of fodder or sugar beet (which can be grown for rabbits) are only suitable after they have been thoroughly wilted as they contain acids when fresh which may cause scouring. Artichokes, beetroot, carrots, turnips and swedes are all palatable, especially carrots. These roots can be grown for the house and any surplus fed to the rabbits; their wilted tops, which are removed before storage, can also be used. Farmers grow particular varieties of carrots for animal feeding which yield heavily but lack the flavour we expect in the domestic carrot, and these can be obtained from agricultural seed merchants. Kale grown for cattle is also an excellent green food yielding plenty of green leaf well into April and possessing a thick stem which, if sliced lengthways in four, provides a particularly nutritious feed. 'Maris Kestrel' is a particularly good variety to grow as it is winter hardy and the stalks are palatable right down to the root. Thousand-headed Kale can be used over a long period by picking the leafy shoots as they are required.

Parts of vegetable plants which would normally be consigned to the compost heap can be utilised by the rabbit, e.g. peapods and spent pea haulms, overgrown runner beans and their haulms in moderation, also french beans. However, broad bean pods are not normally appreciated nor are the spent plants. Tomato leaves are not suitable for rabbits, nor are spent marrow and cucumber leaves. The stem of the

Table 3

Proportions of succulent rabbit feed suitable for garden cultivation

Annual sowing

CATTLE CARROT Sow June–July Single 15 cm (6 in.)	KOHL-RABI Sow February Single 15 cm (6 in.)
PARSNIP Sow March Single 20 cm (9 in.)	MARROWSTEM KALE Sow March–June Single 30 cm (1 ft) (Heavy cropper Not frost resistant)
MANGOLD or FODDER BEET variety 'Red Ottofte' Sow March–April Single 20 cm (9 in.)	
	THOUSAND-HEADED KALE Sow March–June Single 40 cm (15 in.) (Frost resistant Late cropper)
SUGAR BEET Sow March–April Single 20 cm (9 in.)	
	KALE variety 'Maris Kestrel' Sow March–June Single 30 cm (1 ft) (Very palatable stem Frost resistant)

Permanent rows of comfrey and lucerne would be advantageous.
Comfrey: Plant sets 90 cm (3 ft.) apart April.
  Manure heavily. Keep land clean.
  Cut for fodder when flower stems appear.
  Up to six cuts between April and October.

Lucerne: Sow in April 1·3 cm ($\frac{1}{2}$ in.) deep drills
26 cm (10 in.) apart. Manure well. Cut
for hay just as it flowers.

Table 4

Table to show utilisation of garden and hedgerow feed

Month	Food	Remarks
January	Carrots, cabbage, kale ('Maris Kestrel'), sugar beet, fodder beet, mangolds, artichoke, blackberry leaves	Avoid feeding frozen leaf and roots
February	Carrots, cabbage, kale ('Maris Kestrel'), sugar beet, artichoke, fodder beet, mangolds	Avoid feeding frozen leaf and roots
March	Mangolds, kohl-rabi, carrots, kale (thousand-headed), shoots and stalks from brussels sprouts, some hedge parsley, hogweed	Hedge weeds beginning to shoot, feed sparingly
April	Mangolds, kohl-rabi, shoots and stalks from brussels sprouts, kale (thousand-headed), hedge parsley, hogweed, dandelion, chickweed, comfrey, grass	Feed small quantities of a wide variety of weeds to avoid digestive upsets
May	Remaining winter cabbages, hedge parsley, hogweed, plantain, dandelion, chickweed, vetches, comfrey, lucerne, grass	Hedgeweeds in profusion now and very good quality
June	Comfrey, lucerne, vegetable thinnings, lettuce (in moderation), carrots, beetroot, pea pods	Hedge weeds becoming fibrous and beginning to seed especially in dry summer

July	Comfrey, lucerne, vegetable thinnings, pea pods and pea haulms	Hedge weeds only valuable if young. In dry summer weeds will have little value. Grass will be of little value except in damp summer
August	Comfrey, lucerne, waste vegetables, pea haulms, grass (in a wet summer)	Most greenery will now be obtained from the garden
September	Kale, waste vegetables, pea haulms, carrots, parsnip, hedge parsley, comfrey, lucerne, grass	Gradually start winter feed of roots, sparingly at first
October	Cabbage, carrots, parsnip, hogweed, hedge parsley, dandelion, marrowstem kale, grass	Most years hedge weeds will be found this month, but these are generally rather watery and only fed to add variety to roots and kale
November	Cabbage, carrots, parsnip, sugar beet, marrowstem kale, potato peelings (cooked), apple peelings	Grass very watery, chiefly roots
December	Cabbage, carrot, parsnip, sugar beet, marrowstem kale, potato peelings (cooked), apple peelings	Chiefly roots. Kitchen waste in moderation to add variety

cabbage, however, can be left in the ground and cut down half an inch lengthways. These will then sprout again and yield more greenery for the rabbit.

Thinnings from the vegetable garden can form a valuable part of the rabbit's rations. Unwanted brassica plants from the seed beds, root thinnings, e.g. carrots and beetroot, and lettuce thinnings in moderation can all be utilised to advantage. *Avoid plants which have been sprayed or dusted with insecticide.*

Potatoes can form part of the ration of fattening rabbits. They are best fed cooked and then mashed in conjunction with crushed oats to form a crumbly consistency. As the potatoes are high in carbohydrate, avoid giving them to pregnant or lactating does who will need a higher protein diet. Obviously they will not be the sole constituent of the diet but may be fed as one meal in the day with roots and green stuff as the other meal plus hay *ad lib*. One can utilise the small potatoes which inevitably form part of the garden crop.

Extensive Method—Wild Plants. During the summer months there are many weeds that grow in our gardens and along the road sides which provide the variety that keep the rabbits healthy and cut down the cost of a complete pellet ration. Weeds found commonly in the vegetable garden which are useful include chickweed, groundsel, dandelion, shepherd's purse, plantain (both the broad- and narrow-leaved), fat hen and sow thistle. When feeding weeds do try to supply a wide variety at each meal as this will ensure that as many different nutrients are available as possible. For instance the plantain leaf and wilted nettle leaf are particularly high in protein; shepherd's purse is renowned for its astringent properties. In fact it can be gathered in the summer, dried and hung in bundles in a dry and airy outhouse, and then fed to any animal which is showing signs of scouring. A slight upset caused by injudicious feeding can often be helped by feeding this dry plant during winter when it is normally not available.

The younger green stuff gathered before flowering and seeding will contain a higher proportion of protein which is vital for the rabbit's growth and health. Hence wild, spring-gathered foods are generally better quality than those gathered later in the

Table 5
Table showing relative crude protein % content of some weeds, grasses and legumes

Name	% crude protein	Name	% crude protein
Chicory	19	Grasses	12
Comfrey	25		
Dandelion	19		
Hawkbit	19	*Legumes*	
Hogweed	20	Clover	23
Knapweed	20	Lucerne	17
Nettles	27	Trefoil	17
Plantain	20		
Sorrel	25		
Shepherd's purse	27		
Sow thistle	18		
Yarrow	20		

year. After seeding the leaves become more fibrous and unpalatable. Plants which are not allowed to flower will retain their attractiveness longer. This can be achieved by picking the flowering stalks and leaving some of the remaining leaves. However some plants, e.g. groundsel and chickweed, grow from seed to flower in a very short period so that young plants are available throughout the year as long as the conditions are not too unfavourable. As a general rule, aim for gathering the leaves from plants in their youth.

Plants found commonly on the roadside and near hedges which contribute to the rabbit's diet include bramble leaves which are found for most of the year, hogweed, sheep's parsley, vetches, coltsfoot, knapweed, mallow, yarrow, ivy leaves (the flower and berries are poison) cleavers and comfrey. The leaves of the dock plant contain iron which is particularly useful for pregnant and nursing does. I have found that the nursing mother will appreciate a couple of dock leaves at intervals where the empty doe or growing stock will completely ignore them. Dock plants are best avoided as soon as they run up to flower because the seeds are poisonous along with the roots. Dandelion leaves are also appreciated but in moderation as they are liable to encourage excessive urination.

Poisonous plants. Hemlock has been picked by the unwary as it resembles sheep's parsley (which is not poisonous) especially in the spring before the flowing stem is apparent. Both sheep's parsley and hemlock have deeply cut, bright green leaves, but the sheep's parsley stem is green and grooved where the hemlock is smooth and green with obvious purple mottling. The hemlock is generally first found in late April or May while sheep's parsley is often found growing earlier in the year, but the sheep's parsley often shoots again in September after a dry summer when the hemlock is often far less prolific. They both have small white or cream flowers which grow in umbels borne on a metre (2–3 ft) stem. Other poisonous wild plants include bindweed; both the common bindweed found in the garden and hedge bindweed or bellbine, which have large white flowers up to 5 in. or 6 in. across. Also toxic are anemone, all the bryonies, celandine, corncockle, common dog's mercury, foxglove, the nightshades, poppies, scarlet pimpernel, toadflax and wild arum. Many bulbous plants found in gardens are poisonous to rabbits including aconite, autumn crocus, bluebell, daffodil, lily-of-the-valley, tulip and snowdrop. Christmas roses, delphinium and love-in-a-mist are also best avoided. The tree leaves of acacia, box, laburnum, privet and yew are also poisonous while rhubarb leaves and potato haulms can prove fatal.

Lawn mowings. Many people feed lawn mowings but great care is needed here; they can cause scouring if fed after heating and before they have gone yellow. If you must feed this, check that there are no poisonous plants on the lawn, then leave the box off the mower and let the sun dry the grass before feeding it. Mowings can be made into a form of hay, but it is very difficult to get them really dry and stored in such a way as not to become dusty and musty; this can cause respiratory troubles.

Grass. Lawn grass in spring may supply the bulk of the food needed for fattening rabbits in a Morant hutch (see Figure 7) as long as it is moved regularly twice a day. In spring the fast-growing grass is palatable and sufficiently high in protein to supply the needs of the rabbit entirely. If allowed to go to seed the grass ceases to be valuable and will need to be augmented by extra food either green or pelleted. In August or September we experience the autumn flush of grass when the damper weather allows it to sprout once more, but the grass seldom appears to be so attractive and will definitely need to be supplemented by extra rations. Grass grown elsewhere than the lawn can also be a very useful green food as it seldom causes digestive upsets. However, if it is gathered from a heavily fertilised field, care must be taken not to feed too much of it especially in early May as the combination of extra nitrogen and the low fibre content of the plant can cause scours.

Frozen food. Green stuffs and roots should never be fed in a frozen state. Roots are best stored where the frost cannot get to them and if the weather is really cold do not give any more food than can be consumed before it becomes frozen in the hutch.

Wet green food. Many people only feed green stuff dry.

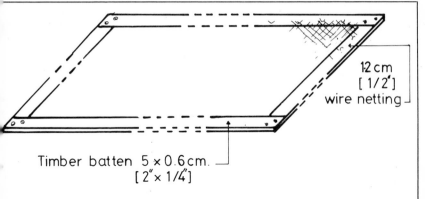

Fig. 21 Wooden frame suitable for drying acorns, nettles, comfrey leaves and wet, green food.

When the food is gathered in rain spread it out thinly in a shed on a frame to drain. I find that if the stock are accustomed to small quantities of wet feed they will not come to any harm, but if fed in large quantities it can cause the rabbits to scour. In the summer, avoid leaving green food in the sack or in a heap as it very rapidly heats and ferments, especially the leguminous plants such as clovers and vetches.

Acorns. Acorns can form a part of the fattening rabbit's rations. Gathered as they fall, they can be dried in a cool airy shed on netting shelves and then stored. They can be fed whole or lightly crushed up to 30 grams (I oz) per day (this is about a normal handful). They should be introduced slowly as they have a bitter taste and contain tannin which can cause constipation.

Rations
As we have seen, it is difficult to lay down hard and fast rules for methods of feeding. When the cost of feeding has to be considered a combination of pellet

59

Table 6
Suggested Rations

These are *guide lines* for the maintenance of a 3·5 kg (8 lb) empty doe, or a buck not being used for service.

Ration I (Extensive feeding)
0·7 kg (1¼ lb) wide variety of young green stuff, weeds and cabbage.

Ration II (Intensive feeding)
113 g (4 oz) proprietary rabbit pellets (in two feeds).

Ration III Combined methods (warmer months)
113 g (4 oz) green food
56 g (2 oz) mixed cereals (lightly crushed oats, rolled barley) in three feeds: cereal a.m., greenstuff midday, cereals p.m.

Ration IV Combined methods (winter months)
170 g (6 oz) roots (mixed)
56 g (2 oz) mixed cereals (lightly crushed oats, rolled barley).

All these rations should be augmented by *ad lib* best hay.
In practice the stockman will adapt these rations to the food he has available.

Fattening ration using mashed cooked potato for a 2·25 kg (5 lb) rabbit
56 g (2 oz) boiled potato
40 g (1½ oz) lightly crushed oats
Ad lib good palatable hay

feeding, homegrown foods and wild plants will suit most situations.

Except when a pelleted food is fed solely, only give as much roots, green feed and straight cereals as will be consumed before the next feed. However, the hayrack must constantly be replenished. Any green feed or cereal left from the previous meal must always be cleared away. Over-feeding may cause the rabbits to go off their feed and in this case cut down the feed and gradually return to normal over a period of a few days. A greedy rabbit offered too much of one type of green stuff which is particularly palatable, e.g. clover, will gorge till its belly is twice the normal size. This may be fatal. Avoid this by feeding a variety of foods and never letting the animals get over-hungry. The good stockman will know which of his rabbits are greedy and which are fastidious feeders. Both types need a varied diet. The former need this to prevent gorging on one type of plant and the latter to tempt the appetite.

Choosing hay
(Bales may weigh on average about 20 kg (40 lb))

Seeds Hay. This is made from the first year's growth from a newly sown grass mixture. It is generally hard and rather spikey for rabbits. However, it often contains clover which has a high protein content. Watch out for mustiness in this type of hay as the long grass and clover leaf are difficult to dry except in perfect haymaking conditions. It is very expensive.

Meadow Hay. This can be made from permanent pasture. It often contains many different grasses and weeds and is generally much softer to the touch. Rabbits may find this far more palatable than seeds hay. Check that there is no ragwort in the field before the hay is cut as this is deadly poisonous even when dried.

Nettle Hay. This is not normally for sale but can be made at home. Nettles are best cut just as they come into flower. Turn them carefully in the evening when the dew will make the valuable leaves less brittle. Cart and store when dry. This may be after two or three days in ideal weather conditions. The hay is valuable for its high protein content.

Straw. In the event of no hay bales being available, spring-sown barley or oat straw will prove a possible replacement. Wheat straw or autumn-sown barley or oat straw is too hard for feed and is only good for litter. Straw is seldom musty and if it is bought from a farm where weed sprays are not used it will contain dried grass and weeds which may be appreciated by the rabbits.

Homemade Hay. Even in the most well-regulated gardens, patches of weed grasses are found. These may not look like a hayfield but can be cut at the best time, about the end of May, just after the grasses come into flower and pollen is seen hanging from each head (later-cut hay is easier to dry and 'make' but will have less feeding value). These small areas can be cut with a hook or scythe and left in windrows to dry. The advantage of this lies in the fact that each patch can be dealt with in five minutes or so, turning the grass windrows over with a rake onto a dry patch several times a day. A heavy crop will need to be shaken using a garden fork. As soon as the grass begins to dry the hay aroma will become very apparent. When the hay is moved it will apparently rattle. This is the stage to 'cock' it where it can 'make' for a week or ten days before being put under cover. The cock is built by placing successive forkfuls of hay in a pile, completing the load with a forkful placed on top like a toupee and raked down all round to act as a hat in case of rain. Hay made like this from all available areas—the sides of little-used roads, friends' gardens etc—will save the expense of buying hay. Haymaking takes a season or so to perfect to avoid a musty sample but that which is unsuitable for feeding can be used as litter. In a wet season or in rainy areas of the country, the hay can be placed on fences to dry. The cut grass is laid over the wires for the wind and fitful sun to dry. This will keep it off the ground which often remains wet all the time.

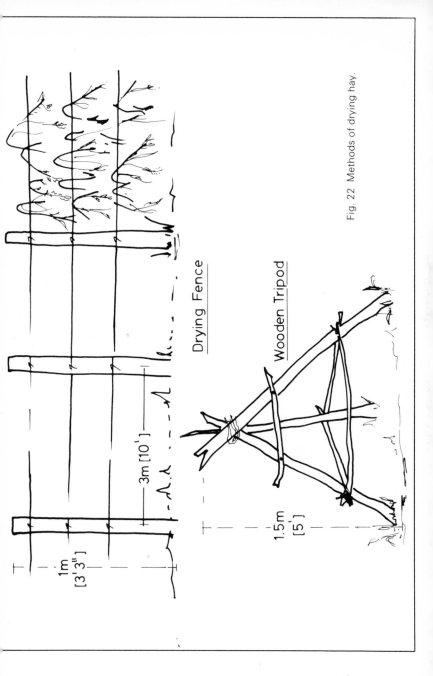

Drying Fence

Wooden Tripod

1m [3' 3"]

3m [10']

1.5m [5']

Fig. 22 Methods of drying hay.

63

Storage

Hay and Straw. These must be stored under cover. Don't place bales directly on a concrete floor but on pieces of wood 60 cm (2 ft) apart to ensure that the air can pass underneath. Nettle hay is best placed on pieces of paper or hemp sacking on top of the wood to save all the broken nettle leaves.

Pellets and Cereals. These are best stored in large biscuit tins or plastic dustbins to keep out vermin and damp.

Green stuffs. Wild foods are best placed on a wooden frame or wire shelf to prevent heating and to aid drying (see Figure 21). This can be placed under cover near the hutches.

Roots. Roots are best harvested when mature. They can be topped and gently placed in a clamp. This can then be covered with straw or bracken and finally topped with a layer of soil 15 cm (6 in.) deep. In the colder parts of the country it may be necessary to build the clamp in a shed to avoid severe frost damage.

Coprophagy

The rabbit's dung is usually passed in one corner of the hutch and consists of firm oval pellets with obvious signs of fibre content. On occasions softer, smoother and possibly longer pellets are passed which are without visible fibrous pieces. These are usually voided at night and normally eaten direct from the anus. It has been found that these pellets contain nearly three times the amount of protein as that of the hard faecal pellets. It is thought that this may be a method of improving the digestion of the proteins in the diet.

4 Breeding

Between mating and the birth of the young, approximately thirty-one days must elapse, but before she is launched into maternity we must be sure that the doe will be capable of carrying up to eight or nine embryo rabbits to full term, as well as standing the strains of the subsequent period of lactation. The young maiden doe must be well fed but not too fat, obviously in good condition with a bright clear eye, smooth shiny coat and a clean vent. Check that there is no visible evidence of malocclusion of the teeth (see page 125). She must also have eight obviously functional teats (though from five to ten are not unusual); 15 per cent of does may have one or more blind teats and these are usually the ones well up between the front paws. Another point frequently overlooked is the length of her claws. See that they are reasonably short as this will avoid lameness or damage to the young (see page 127).

Training the doe

The newly acquired doe having been bought at about three months of age will have about two months to settle in, become accustomed to her new surroundings, possibly to undergo a change of feed and also more importantly to get to know her new handler before being mated at approximately five months of age. The young does will benefit from daily handling as soon as they appear to have settled down. This initial acclimatisation can be hastened by a constant patter of conversation in a calm unhurried manner while the animals are being fed and tended. People are often inclined to underestimate the influence of the human voice on animals. As the rabbits become accustomed to their handler, it will be noticed that they will hop to the front of their cages with their noses twitching and ears pricked forward. This is the time to gently put a hand in the hutch talking reassuringly all the time. Let the rabbits sniff at it and before long the majority will enjoy being stroked. Practise carrying the does about. This early training will ensure that they are quieter and calmer when being taken to visit the buck and may improve the chance of a successful mating. Accustom the does to ride calmly on the arm with their noses facing the handler and rumps resting on the hand so that they can be placed in the buck's hutch in a suitable position for him to mount with the least amount of effort. The does must always be *taken to the buck* and not vice versa as they may easily attack the buck visiting their cages.

Readiness for mating

A successful mating is often the result of introducing the doe to the buck when she appears to be ready for it. In this case the doe will show signs of restlessness, hopping about the cage when she is obviously not particularly hungry. She may stamp with her hind feet and then sit up on her haunches obviously listening with her nose twitching in an effort to catch the scent of her mate. She may even go so far as to pluck the fur from her dewlap and between her front legs to build a nest.

Training the buck

Training will not stop with the doe; the buck also needs plenty of firm handling. He must learn to accept the human hand in his hutch especially when he has a doe with him. In this way a potentially excitable doe can be reassured and calmed. This may possibly prevent a lot of unnecessary rushing around and frustration on the part of the buck and resultant infertility.

The buck's hutch

It is best kept within sight of the does' but in the lowest one of the hutches if they are tiered, as a keen buck will often spray passers-by (especially strangers) with urine. As with many species of male animal his urine contains a higher proportion of ammonia than that of the female. Great care must be taken over the hygiene of his hutch or the resulting atmosphere may cause his eyes to become puffy and may also affect his respiration.

Mating

The doe is introduced to the buck's hutch, rump first as previously described. If he is ready to mate and she is in good mating condition (lifts her tail when stroked across her rump) he will mount her and mating will take place with little more ado. A successful mating is following by the buck falling off to one side with his ears back. Some bucks will grunt or squeal but others are quite silent. The doe is then gently and quietly removed, holding her rump up rather than down to help retain the semen, and replaced in her own hutch.

Management of the buck

A buck will need enough food to keep him in first-class condition without being too fat. Over-fatness can result in infertility. The underfed buck will produce less vigorous sperm at each ejaculation and this may result in small litters. A young buck must be checked to see that both his testes have descended into the scrotum, also that the reproductive parts and the anus are obviously clean and healthy. His claws must be regularly clipped if they are long (see page 127). A basically fertile buck's performance is influenced heavily by his good management. The young buck will want no more than one doe a week, but as he gets older he can cope with more. However, he will seldom get overworked in our domestic rabbitry. Keep a really sharp eye on his general condition and attitude and where there are only three or four does he must not be allowed to get too fat and lethargic by overfeeding. On the other hand don't starve him. A buck with a limited number of wives will not require *ad lib* feeding and, depending on his size and work, will require between 112 and 140 g of pellets (that is 4 to 5 oz) a day. A buck fed on a mixed diet will require less of the fattening foods like cooked potatoes but more of the high-quality young green stuff. Do pander to his obvious likes and dislikes bearing in mind that his needs are vital.

The buck's handling must be sympathetic and gentle; his first mating is best done in the evening when all is quiet. His hutch will already be out of the direct light of a window (excessive light can cause low fertility). His subsequent performance may be affected by his first mating so see that the doe is well handled, quiet and yet obviously in mating condition. This will ensure that he has every chance of a successful mating. As soon as the doe is removed give him his evening feed and leave him in peace. An initial quiet and successful mating will set the pattern for his subsequent work.

Problems

Lack of desire to mate may be caused by incorrect feeding; too much, too little, or not enough good-quality food. He may be under a direct light. There may be too much going on around him, so confine mating to the evenings when it is usually quieter. On the other hand though, even if he is willing the doe may not be mature enough. Some rabbits not bred especially for meat do not mature until seven or eight months. However, try the hand over the rump test before offering her to the buck. The doe may be too fat and thus inaccessible, resulting in the buck failing to mate successfully and becoming frustrated. As we can see, he must be watched carefully all the time to see that he is kept in tiptop condition. He may retain his potency for four or five years but latterly smaller litters from all the does might indicate that a replacement buck is needed.

Pregnancy

Having replaced the doe in her hutch after mating, feed her and see that she is obviously not unconfortable. Fill in her record card with the date, time of mating and name of buck. This is so often overlooked. She will now continue her previous rations of about 112 g (4 oz) of pellets per day in two feeds if fed intensively. If she is fed on an extensive mixed diet, continue to feed a variety of high-quality green stuff, avoiding old wilted or heated food and too much fattening roots of one kind which may possibly lack some vital requirement. She will continue to be fed like this until the third week of her pregnancy when the rabbit foetuses will have started to make considerable demands on her. She can now be fed to appetite with a plentiful supply of high-quality green stuff.

Pregnancy diagnosis

In order that the doe is not overfed it is necessary to know if she really *is* pregnant. A fairly reliable method is to feel her mammary glands. About twenty-four days after mating the doe will normally exhibit a certain thickening of the flesh around the two rows of teats. Very gently run a finger down the teat line having previously done this on an empty doe for comparison. The pregnant doe's teats may be more prominent and the flesh behind them fuller than in the empty doe. A more difficult method of pregnancy diagnosis is the one that is best learnt from watching an experienced handler. This is known as palpation. At about the fourteenth day the young will be about the size of large marbles. The novice will find that an older doe will be easier to diagnose as the muscles of her abdomen will naturally be slacker than those of the maiden. Place the doe on a non-slippery surface on the handling table, holding her gently but firmly by the ears and the loose skin on her shoulders. Run the other hand under her abdomen in front of the pelvis and between her legs and *gently* feel with the thumb on one side of the abdomen and the fingers on the other. At fifteen days the embryos or unborn rabbits will be distinguishable from the faecal pellets which are smaller and lie higher up the abdomen. *Very gently* move the fingers and thumb back and forward and the embryos will be large enough to slip between them and will feel like a chain of marbles. Great care must be practised when doing this or the young may be damaged or at worst the doe may abort (produce young prematurely). The experienced handler will be able to diagnose pregnancy in this manner at about nine days. The doe must not be frightened during palpation, in order to avoid tenseness which could damage the embryos.

Feeding

We are now almost sure that the doe is pregnant so around the twenty-first day of pregnancy her rations will need to be doubled as the young grow extremely fast at this stage. The increased demands of the embryos *must* be met. Besides building up condition for lactation, a sufficiency of the best food available is necessary for good milk production. If a solely pelleted ration is fed it will be enough to double the weight of each feed. When feeding greenstuff and grain do be sure that the quality of the food is the best you can obtain and avoid too much bread and potatoes, which are fattening.

Nest boxes

Some rabbit breeders like to allow the doe the opportunity to keep her young in a dark box which will have been put in her hutch as soon as she is mated. A box 30 cm by 50 cm by 30 cm (12 in. × 20 in. × 12 in.) will be suitable. It need not have a lid. The entrance must be large enough for the pregnant doe to enter without damaging or bruising herself. The box will supply the need of most does to kindle (give birth) in the dark and also keep the young warm and in one spot. A hutch with a separate sleeping compartment will not need this nest box.

The box lid will need to be constructed in such a manner that it can be easily cleaned and disinfected between kindlings. Some breeders prefer to use a cardboard box which can be thrown away after each litter, to cut down the risk of disease transmission.

Kindling

The doe will carry the young from twenty-eight to thirty-three days but normally they are born on the thirty-first day after mating. A day or two before she is due to kindle she may well show signs of restlessness or even go off her food. Do check that she has plenty to drink as preparation of the nest will make her thirsty as well as the need to have plenty of milk for her young. Her nest box or breeding compartment will need to be lined with wood shavings or clean, mould-free, soft meadow hay. Straw is not so suitable as it is hard and not such a good insulator. During the last week keep a careful check on the litter in the nesting area, as if it has been fouled by urine she will not use it and may have her young out in the open.

Kindling often takes place at night when all is quiet. However, the nest which will have been prepared by plucking the fur from her breast and dewlap and mixing this with the litter, may have been started a day or so beforehand. A glance will tell if the young have been born as the movements of the hairless blind babies will make the wall of the nest gently heave. The well-handled good-tempered doe will not resent the arrival of her handler. Much is made of the fact that a disturbed nest will encourage the mother to eat the young. I have never seen this happen, even when a six-year-old brought a 'sausage baby' indoors to show her grandmother. The blind and naked two-day-old rabbit was then carefully replaced in its nest by the proud owner of the rabbit. This is a perfect example of the rabbit of gentle temperament trusting its young owner. I do not advise such a bold treatment of the young unless you are completely confident that the doe will not mind this treatment. However, it is a good idea to check the newly born young, but do prepare for this by feeding the doe something particularly succulent to distract her. Next rub some excreta on your hand before gently moving back the fur covering the babies and checking the number born, removing any dead, undersized, or obviously deformed young. Replace the fur carefully. An average litter will consist of about six to seven, but litters do vary ranging from one to about thirteen or fourteen.

A young and careless mother may produce her young anywhere but in the nest, and these will rapidly chill and die unless collected together and replaced in the nest. The doe generally feeds her young when all is quiet (it often appears that she never even visits the young!). But if she is disturbed while suckling she may hop out of the nest and scurry about with one or more young depending from the teats. These she will replace if she is an experienced and good mother, but a young doe may well be too agitated to put the young back. These will have to be replaced. Take the precaution, as before, to rub the hand in some excreta before replacing the babies to avoid the risk of the mother rejecting them.

Cannibalism

Sometimes after the doe has obviously kindled, it will be found that there are no babies present in the nest. This can be a case of cannibalism where the doe has eaten the young as soon as they were born and it can be caused by lack of water to drink during kindling. The doe may be frightened just as she kindles, and when cleaning the young as they are born, accidentally bites ones of the babies and then proceeds to eat them, apparently not being able to distinguish between membrane and young. A difficult kindling can cause extreme stress where she attacks the cause of her pain and consequently eats the young.

I know of one case of *apparent* cannibalism where the doe had kindled in the corner of her hutch. While making her nest she had obviously scratched a knot in the floor which was big enough for the babies to fall through as they were born. Luckily the newborn young were soon found in the lower hutch and restored to the mother, the hole was mended and the doe reared the complete litter.

Fostering

In the event of the doe having an extremely large litter or dying from an injury within four days of kindling, the young may be fostered by another doe with young of the same age. It can be a success if their ages differ by no more than two or three days. Never attempt to save the young from an obviously diseased doe as there is a chance that the infection will have been transmitted to the foster litter. Obviously the combined litters will not want to number more than seven or eight young. The foster doe must be known to be 'milky' and of course be a good mother. Sprinkle the young to be fostered with some damp litter from the foster hutch and carefully put them in the nest, having previously distracted the foster mother's attention with some particularly succulent morsel.

Feeding the lactating doe

At kindling the doe will be consuming around 225 g (8 oz) of pellets a day if fed *ad lib* which will increase to a peak consumption of 500 g (1 lb 2 oz) or even 750 g (1 lb 11 oz) at about three weeks. If the doe is a good mother with plenty of milk the young will remain in the nest longer than the babies of a poor milker. However, at just under three weeks all the young will be out of the nest and nibbling their mother's food. At ten days of age they will have begun to open their eyes and the fine almost invisible short down which covered them at birth will have grown to the normal length proportional to their size and age. Weaning at three to four weeks will mean that the doe's ration must be reduced to 110 g (4 oz) or she may get over-fat and fail to conceive once more. If a mixed diet is used, only the best must be fed. In winter, feed young green stuff including cabbage or kale and a few good-quality roots, e.g. carrots. In the spring and summer, good-quality young wild green stuff augmented by thinnings from the vegetable patch will be possibilities. These must be fed to appetite, and do always have good hay available. It will be advantageous if the doe is fed at least three times daily on this extensive method of feeding. Throughout the lactating period she must have fresh clean water continually available to ensure maximum milk production.

Hand-feeding young rabbits

In the event of no foster mother being available, the soft-hearted will want to attempt hand-feeding. This is a time-consuming operation with the risk of scours through chilling and consequently death; improper milk mixture and over- or under-feeding is very common. I have done this although it is not recommended. I used the quill of a chicken's wing feather (using a fresh one each time for reasons of hygiene). Warm some cow's milk to which a small quantity of beaten egg has been added (rabbit's milk contains up to four times the protein of cow's milk), suck the milk up the quill then holding a finger over the feather end put the quill (which should have the tip cleanly cut off) gently between the rabbit's lips. If it is going to suck it will do so quite quickly. Release the finger at the top of the feather at intervals to allow the milk to escape. Remove the quill as soon as the rabbit appears to stop sucking. Goat's milk will give better results as it is more easily digested, or even a full-cream dried babies' milk following instructions on the tin. In the absence of chicken feathers, a bicycle valve rubber is good but must be cleaned very carefully between feeds. Under-feeding is safer than over-feeding and two feeds a day will emulate the doe. Be prepared to wipe the anus of the babies with a piece of cotton wool to remove any faeces. Hand rearing is not an occupation to be entered upon lightly as it so often results in death, or poor weak stock, which seldom repay the effort invested in them.

Pseudo-pregnancy

A doe which starts to build a nest at sixteen to seventeen days after mating may well be experiencing a pseudo-pregnancy. She will even increase the size of her belly and produce milk. She is not carrying young, but at this stage is highly fertile and a visit to the buck once more will possibly result in a normal pregnancy ensuing. Pseudo-pregnancy can often be brought on just by the sight of a buck or even two does being left together after maturity is reached. They may mount each other. In this case wait till sixteen to seventeen days after they have been separated for a possible pseudo-pregnancy to occur. The following very fertile period will, we hope, precipitate a successful mating. A mature doe which has developed a pattern of regular breeding seldom experiences pseudo-pregnancies.

Heat or oestrus

The rabbit, unlike many large animals, has no regular heat periods. After maturity has been reached the sight or smell of a buck, or just maturity combined with increasing day length, may make her think she is pregnant. She will normally ovulate about six hours after mating, and if this is successful the sperm will fertilise the ova which have been released and a normal pregnancy will follow. In the event of the doe failing to conceive in spite of successive matings, hormone treatment from the vet may be obtained but this is very expensive. It is far better to breed for fertility and cull the infertile does.

Table 7

Table of suggested matings for domestic meat production

Mate	Kindle	Wean
January	February	March
April	May	June
July	August	September
October	November	December

Frequency of mating

Table rabbits which have been bred commercially, provided they do not experience any day-length less than sixteen hours throughout the year, are able to be mated three weeks after kindling. This is another particularly fertile period. The doe will thus be able to produce five to six litters per year. This is really only suitable with good table-bred rabbits which are fed solely on a proprietary rabbit pellet giving adequate nutrition for this high level of production. Some commercial breeders even re-mate four to ten days after kindling when the young are weaned at three weeks. This calls for an extremely high standard of management. I do not recommend this system for the domestic producer; the family will be heartily sick and tired of rabbit—rissole for breakfast, pâté for lunch and pie for supper in order to keep up with the production! Four matings a year will supply plenty of rabbit meat from the three does with a surplus to provide pin money from the sale of fatstock in the market or dressed rabbit to neighbours.

5 Rearing

Weaning time

This varies according to the particular breeding scheme that has been adopted. The commercial breeder who aims to produce six or seven litters a year from each doe may wean the young as early as three weeks of age.

Our domestic rabbits, experiencing a less high-powered breeding programme, will probably be expected to produce a mere four litters annually, which will mean that the young may remain with their dams a little longer. However, if left much more than five weeks with their mothers, they will be needing *ad lib* pellet feeding or a very large quantity of green feed, roots, cereals and hay. The doe may well get too fat resulting in subsequent conception proving elusive. To wean is to accustom the young animal to the loss of its mother's milk. This involves removing the young from their mother with the least stress possible, avoiding chilling.

Chilling

Ideally the weaners will be housed in a separate house where the temperature is warmer than that of the breeding area, thus the risk of chilling is cut to a minimum. Check windows and doors to avoid cold draughts in chilly winter weather. Excessive temperatures in a very hot summer, when appetites may be reduced owing to the heat and consequent lethargy of the animals, can be reduced by the careful manipulation of windows and doors. Weaners kept in outdoor hutches will need to be cossetted in cold wintry conditions. See that the hutch is out of the direct north wind and that there is an overhang to keep the worst of the driving rain or snow at bay. Ensure an adequate supply of litter to compensate the young for the loss of their mother's body heat. Dry hay fluffed up in the sleeping compartment will help to keep the young rabbits warm. This bedding will need changing daily in cold weather. Add fresh hay or straw even twice a day to the sleeping area. Rabbits nibble litter freely, and what is a fluffy warm bed one moment can be reduced very soon to a few nibbled 5 cm (2 in.) lengths of straw or hay the next, and this will afford them little warmth. A chilled litter will fail to thrive and at worst will die unexpectedly.

Feeding

In order that the shock of removal is kept to a

minimum the use of standard feeding and drinking equipment in both breeding and rearing hutches will help to keep the young eating. The weight of the newly weaned rabbits may well remain static for a week, but provided you supply them with adequate good food and warm dry housing, the young will soon adapt to their new surroundings. If pellet feeding is employed, the same ration they may have had while they were with their mother will be available to them in the weaning hutch, but it must be available *all the time* to ensure a large enough intake for maximum growth. There must be adequate trough space, sufficient for all the young to feed at one time. Enough space at four weeks will be very inadequate by six weeks so it is wise to allow what will appear to be too much room at first, to allow for growth. Insufficient space will encourage bullying and consequent un-evenly sized litters. Remember a trough which can be used from both sides (see page 41) will need to be only half as long as one which can only be fed from one side.

Green food fed to young rabbits must consist of that to which they were accustomed when they were still with their dams, to cut down the risk of digestive upsets with consequent possible scouring. Owing to the fact that the young rabbits are no longer having milk they may well gorge and over-feed and a wide variety of good-quality food must be freely available. Remember to put the green stuff where it cannot be trampled under foot. Good-quality hay must be available all the time to augment the green stuff, roots and cereals. If the young are fed crushed oats in the morning, then at mid-day they can be offered green stuff—clean, dry and unfrosted—and in the evening they can be offered more cereal and some roots which will keep them occupied during the night. Be particularly careful to remove any uneaten green stuff or roots before the next feed. If feeding pellets in a self-dusting hopper, the older ones will always be eaten first, but pellets and cereals fed in a simple bowl or trough will need to be checked at each feed to see that the container is clean and unfouled and that there is no accumulation of dust or chaff. Check also that the *food is actually being eaten*. If there is some cereal not being consumed I like to give it to the chickens or pigs and start afresh by washing the container, drying it carefully and refilling it once more with fresh food. If there is any left which is still clean put it to one side and refill to prevent the stale food being left underneath.

Water

It is essential that the same watering equipment the young used with their dam is employed in the weaning hutch. Lack of liquid may prevent the young rabbits feeding. In cold weather it is well worth offering warm water twice daily. In excessively hot weather the rabbits will appreciate frequent cool, fresh water.

Moving the young rabbits

Taking the young from their dam provides an excellent opportunity to handle each one carefully to inspect for disease or abnormality, to weigh them, and consequently to fill in the dam's record card. Make sure the weaner hutch is prepared with adequate litter, water, food and quietness. If the doe has been well handled and is nicely tempered the young will take their cue from her and will accept the handling. Obviously they will hop about to avoid capture; all the young animals enjoy using their bodies to the utmost, and may regard the whole operation as an enormous game. If the doe is young and a little temperamental, it may be worth moving her temporarily to another hutch. Bring the handling table covered with an old blanket or hessian sack tacked on, over to the hutch. Scales or spring balance, a suitable box for holding the young, and a pencil and notebook will be needed. It will help if two people can be available. As each rabbit is weighed, record the weight and then check each rabbit. Are the eyes and nose clean and dry, the teeth not obviously deformed, both ears undamaged? Check the claws on each foot that they are not too long or deformed. Look at the vent to see that it is free from dung and disease, though it may be a little wet around the tail due to the rabbits having urinated in their possible fright. The total number of healthy young, their combined weights and any abnormalities must be recorded on the dam's record card. This information, including date, number of rabbits, weight at weaning and a column for comments and deaths, will then be transferred to the new record card and attached to the weaning hutch.

Rearing

Growth. Growth of the young rabbits will depend on the breed of the rabbit, the number of young that were in the litter, the time of year, the quality and variety of the food supplied, and finally but not least, the general standard of management and the environment.

Hutch Space. Throughout the rearing period the hutch which allows 900 sq. cm (1 sq. ft) of space for each rabbit will be adequate.

Sexing. This is not normally necessary in a litter which is destined for the table. The commercial table breeds will yield a 2 kg (4½ lb) live-weight rabbit for killing from as early as eight weeks of age, so there is little likelihood of undue bullying between the sexes

Fig. 23 Weighing rabbits.

and segregation is therefore unnecessary. However, if potential breeding stock are required or there is a potential show animal these will need to be sexed, removed and housed in separate hutches. Sexing is possible at a few days of age though one needs the aid of a watchmaker's glass in this case. Unless great care is taken, the delicate organs could easily be damaged. The more usual time is at about eight weeks of age or older when the animals not wanted for breeding are killed for the table.

I like to sit on a stool holding the rabbit on my lap with its head towards me. I gently but firmly hold it on its back while it lies along my legs. I hold its two back legs with my hands above the hocks and when the rabbit is relaxed, my two thumbs can move to the vent area and very gently press either side. The distance between the anus and the penis is further than that between the anus and the vulva of the doe. At six weeks the organs of the male and the female appear very similar to the novice, but as the animal gets older the penis of the male, a slightly raised round tip, will be clearly seen when the vent area is gently pressed, but the female will show as a slit-like aperture. The teats will be apparent in both male and female at this stage. As the young rabbit reaches sexual maturity the scrotum will be clearly seen either side of the penis in the males.

The head of the male is broader and larger than that of the female and it is usually more masculine and dominant in its attitude.

Fattening

Growing and fattening are synonymous in the table rabbit. The longer the animal takes to reach table weight the more it will have cost to produce; it will also have been using hutch space which could have either been housing more rabbits or, more important,

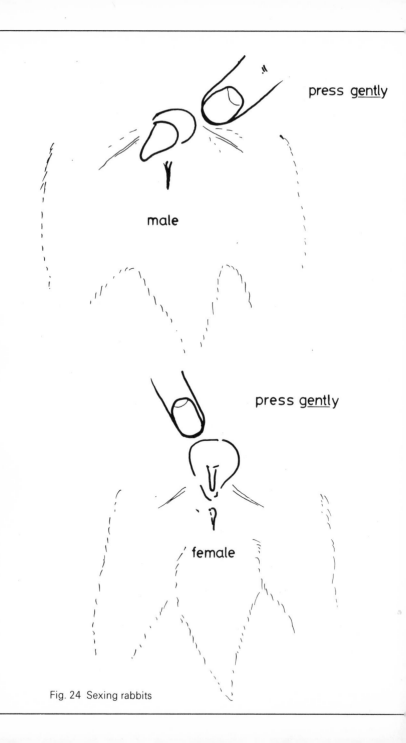

press gently

male

press gently

female

Fig. 24 Sexing rabbits

using a hutch which would have benefited from a thorough clean-out and subsequent 'rest' from use (see page 137).

The aim in table-rabbit production is fast growth using well-reared youngsters from a milky doe. The young from a doe with poor mothering instincts and low milk production will be less likely to 'dress-out' favourably. The weight of the carcase in proportion to the live weight will be low in spite of adequate feeding and management after weaning. The rabbits will have less muscle on the bone and will appear to have a rather large head in proportion to the body. They may also appear pot-bellied, carrying an apparently larger load of intestines than their better-reared peers. These rabbits will have eaten as much food as the well-nurtured young rabbits but will produce far less meat. They may also tend to run to fat if they are fed really well after weaning.

From this we can see that the young from a milky dam will be more profitable, efficiently utilising their food which will have been used to produce a meaty carcase. This type will obviously be more satisfactory to the producer of show or fancy stock as well.

Intensive feeding

For maximum growth an intensive method of feeding will produce the fastest results. Aim for 2·25 kg (5 lb) carcases from good table stock at eight weeks of age. The same stock fed extensively may take three months or more to reach this killing weight. *Ad lib* pellet feeding calls for acute observation by the feeder. If a gravity-fed hopper is used (see page 42) always check twice a day that the trough underneath is full of pellets; that the food flow is not impeded by hay, dusty broken pellets or moisture which can form a cake of souring pellets. Note at the same time that the water supply is clean, change it daily, especially in hot weather—*a thirsty rabbit won't eat*. Watch for boredom caused by the animal assuaging its appetite quickly, then bullying, chewing the hutch or fur eating. A well-filled hay rack full of best-quality hay and a plentiful supply of fresh bedding to nibble will prevent this happening. An even-sized litter is less likely to suffer in this way.

Extensive feeding

If it is at all possible thrice daily feeding will produce better results than twice a day, as the animals will have the incentive of fresh food to stimulate their appetites. The growth rates resulting from this method of feeding are dependent on the quality of the food. In spring the availability of good-quality, high-protein green stuff will produce better performance than during the winter when a more limited supply and variety of greenery is available. Do make sure that any stale food is *meticulously* removed from the previous feed. During spring a constant variety of greenery at each feed will help to prevent scours and digestive upsets which can result from a feed being made up entirely of one kind of plant (e.g. clover). Animals will seldom suffer from a surfeit of grass unless it is gathered from a source which has been heavily dressed with a nitrogenous artificial fertiliser (e.g. nitro chalk or even sulphate of ammonia).

Fat

Rabbits are renowned for their relatively fat-free carcases. A well-reared, fast-grown, killing-weight rabbit will carry little fat and what there is will be most apparent around the kidneys. For some reason the British consumer does not appreciate yellow fat in his meat. This taste is not confined to the fat of rabbits as the fat of both beef and fowl meat is preferred when it is white or creamy coloured. However the pheasant may carry its yellow pigment to the table with pride! If the surplus rabbits from our rabbit concern are to be sold it may be worth buying breeding stock which is known to carry the genes for white fat. The ability to breed yellow-coloured fat is inherited. The yellow-fatted rabbit may barely show any yellow pigmentation if grown fast and killed at an early age. The colour of fat however will be more apparent in these animals if fed a preponderance of green stuff, carrots or maize.

Hardness of fat

This seems to be dependent on the speed of growth of the animal. The faster the growth the harder the fat. In winter the fat tends to be harder than in those rabbits killed during the summer. This may be caused by the nature of the food, more roots and the fibrous nature of the hay and lower proportion of green stuff. A fattening ration consisting of a high proportion of flaked maize may produce a softer fat than stock fattened on pellets or oats and rolled barley.

Taints in flesh. A high proportion of cabbage and kale fed to fattening rabbits in the last few weeks of life may tend to give the flesh a 'cabbagy' flavour. Avoid feeding a pelleted ration known to contain large quantities of fish meal.

Rearing for breeding

As soon as the fat rabbits are removed from the litter, any stock earmarked for future replacement breeders must be reduced to 110 g (4 oz) of pellets daily if fed intensively, or feeding so that the animal is 'sharp' when fed (looking for food, having cleared its previous feed) twice a day. This will prevent over-fatness which, as we know, often leads to sterility at worst or small litter numbers.

Selection of breeders

Only select replacement breeders from the stock of a good buck and doe. The doe must have produced several litters of at least six young reared to killing weight and these young must produce good meaty carcases at an early age. The dam of replacement stock must also have the ability to conceive during the winter as well as the warmer months and produce young free from inherited deformities, e.g. malocclusion of the teeth (see page 125) and yellow fat.

6 The Harvest

To the young, perhaps the most important product of keeping rabbits is the pleasure they generate. This pleasure gained from tending the well-loved pet rabbit is absorbing and satisfying. We learn responsibility and consideration, and also to be observant.

The satisfaction gained from rearing a healthy, happy animal, and successfully breeding from it, with little effort can lead to producing meat for the table. The rabbit carcase lends itself to endless variations of the culinary art as well as the production of pelts and not least the inevitable byproduct of a continual supply of high-quality and comparatively dry manure which will enrich any soil and will improve its moisture-retaining properties (see page 139).

If rabbits are kept for showing, the young which fail to reach the required standard for the show pen can be fattened and killed for the house thus helping to justify the time spent with the rabbit community. Most breeds bred for show may take longer to fatten than purpose-bred table animals, and will often have smaller litters. They will possibly have difficulty breeding in the darkest months of the year. Their carcases may not be so uniformly meaty and the texture in some is inclined to be coarse.

Age to kill

The size of carcase will depend on the requirements of the cook, the economic age to kill and whether the skin is to be utilised in the production of cured pelts. It has been found that a 2·0 to 2·5 kg ($4\frac{1}{2}$ to 5 lb) rabbit will produce a 1 kg ($2\frac{1}{4}$ lb) carcase. This supplies conveniently sized joints. The commercial meat breeds may reach the weight at eight weeks of age, but the fancy breed produced for particular features of shape and fur may take much longer and of course the tiny breeds, e.g. Netherland Dwarf and the Polish breed, which mature at 1 kg ($2\frac{1}{2}$ lb) will barely make a lunch for two. The rabbit will give us prime meat up to about ten months of age providing it has not been used for breeding. But this rabbit will also have eaten a vast quantity of food and taken up valuable hutch space.

Killing

To ensure that the animal's gut is reasonably empty (making eventual evisceration a less messy operation) it is reasonable to withhold food for at least eight hours before killing. In order that the meat will cool as quickly as possible to slow down the putrefaction process, it is a good plan to kill in late afternoon or evening. During summer this also cuts down the risk of fly blow. Though the animal has all food removed for this period it *must* have normal access to the usual clean water supply which helps prevent distress and possible dehydration.

Killing is a knack best learnt from someone who is experienced. This is a job that can be done perfectly easily and humanely by a normally strong adult man or woman. I have always maintained that any bird or animal killed when it is obviously not distressed will taste better and this has recently been scientifically proved. My children used to gaze in wonder as I talked affectionately to a rabbit or fowl while I calmed it prior to the dastardly deed. Not until the creature has ceased to struggle, its eye is calm and it is resting confidently in your arms while you murmur sweet nothings, can you gently move it to the position for killing. This may seem quite ghoulish but it also, strangely enough, reduces the possible distress to the killer caused by the frantic strugglings of the creature. There are two recognised methods of killing rabbits. One will be familiar especially to those who have killed fowls, and involves dislocation of the neck. The left hand firmly holds the rabbit's back legs between hock and tail while the other hand strokes the creature's back and then gradually grasps the neck from the back and while stretching the neck, tilts the chin backwards with a sharp jerk which dislocates it with very little effort. This should result in instantaneous death. Frantic pulling indicates that the *action* is incorrect and results in struggles by the rabbit. One or two rabbits killed under the eagle eye of an experienced killer will give confidence. Another way which I have employed when killing wild rabbits hideously swollen with myxomatosis, is to replace the hand on the neck and chin by a sharp blow behind the ears with a stout stick. Personally I do not favour this method as my aim is not all that accurate but it serves when the neck is swollen and too large for a female hand to grasp.

The next method saves the effort of calming the upturned rabbit suspended by its back legs. The rabbit is placed on a convenient table or bench (covered with a sack to prevent sliding). Stand sideways to the animal as it faces to the left with the

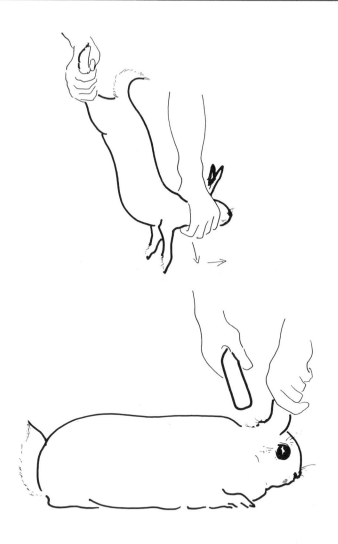

Fig. 25 Two methods of killing a rabbit.

operator's hand firmly but gently holding its ears up. The animal is then hit behind the ears on the neck with a short stout stick, or I find the side of my hand, karate fashion, brought down sharply will kill the animal. Whatever method is employed a certain amount of twitching and kicking will ensue for a moment or two. This can be distressing to children unless they have had the process explained. A dislocated neck can be felt readily, especially if the neck of a live rabbit has been felt for comparison. The dislocated bones feel crooked and unnaturally aligned.

Skinning

I shall never forget, as a child, watching my great uncle skin wild rabbits which we had caught while out with the ferret. On catching the rabbits in the nets we disentangled the struggling creatures and rapidly dislocated their necks, there being no time for calming the creatures; they would most likely have escaped with a Houdini-like wriggle. The next process was to empty their bladders. Holding the still wriggling dead rabbit between our knees we pressed the animals lower abdomen downwards with a stroking motion which emptied the bladder. I soon learnt why, when I later eviscerated (removed the gut) one whose bladder I had forgotten to empty. My ham-fisted attempts at removing the intestine punctured the bladder and efficiently sprayed me and the carcase with strong-smelling urine. Lesson learnt. The next job was to hamstring the creature by inserting a sharp pointed knife between the tendon of the back leg and the muscle above the hock and putting the other leg through the hole. The body could then be hung head down from a nail or hook to drain the blood to the head.

After five minutes' hanging, sufficient blood would

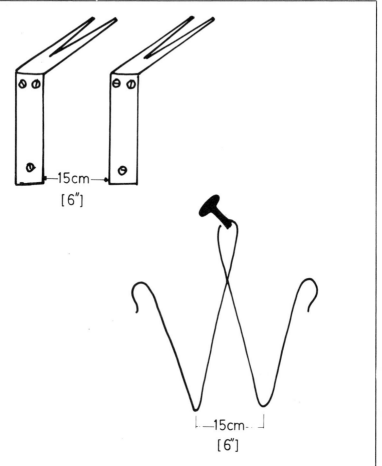

Fig. 26 Two types of leg holder. The back legs are dropped into the loop and held by the hock joint.

have gravitated to the neck to leave a relatively light coloured carcase. The skin was then removed while the body was still warm which assisted the process enormously. A sharp knife was inserted into the abdomen near the hind legs taking care not to puncture the intestine. Cutting the muscle wall over the abdomen, splitting up as far as the rib cage, and a shake by the back legs followed by the rabbit being turned up the other way holding the head, we loosened the contents of the abdomen and the rabbit was then laid down. Two fingers were then inserted in the cavity between the hind legs to pull away the rectum and the bladder. The process was repeated in the chest cavity leaving the heart but loosening the lungs which were always well attached. A final shake and all the viscera (with luck) would fall out leaving the kidneys in place, also the heart, and possibly the liver. The liver was then relieved of its gall bladder, a small sausage-like dark-greenish organ (if punctured it will release a greenish gall fluid which can heavily taint all it touches). The gall bladder was cut away with a sharp knife and removed carefully.

The actual skinning process my uncle completed with the aid of chopper and chopping block in less than thirty seconds! The head, front and back legs were held on the block and chopped off (the legs at the joints). Then he put his hand between the fur and the carcase starting at the abdomen. Holding the pelt in one hand and the carcase in the other he pulled; thereby undressing the unfortunate beast with one swift movement. This carcase was then washed under the pump and thrown unceremoniously in its entirety into a large pan with a carrot, an onion, a few herbs, salt and water. This was placed in the oven to simmer all day. I have never tasted better rabbit stew to this day. The viscera were eagerly consumed by the sheep dogs. Stretched carefully the skin was then nailed up on the inside wall of a wooden shed, flesh side out, to dry before eventual collection by a dealer. The dry and draughty surroundings dried the skin in days.

Conventional skinning

Having killed the rabbit hang the carcase (see page 93) by the hind legs, with the animal's back to the wall. The height at which the carcase hangs depends on the height of the operator. Leave the blood to drain to the neck for five minutes. If the carcase is to be bled (to assist the whitening of the flesh, though this is not vital) cut the neck with a sharp knife at the jugular vein and place a container under the carcase to collect the blood. Cut the skin round below the hocks with a really sharp pointed knife, then continue the cut to the vent on the inside of both legs. With a finger loosen the skin round the hocks and cut off the tail. Then pull the skin sleeve fashion down to the neck pulling out the front legs like arms from a jumper. The front paws are then severed with the knife. As the skin is drawn over the head a firm cut at the base of each ear will release the head skin except on the forehead down to the nose which may need a little help with a sharp knife.

Evisceration or Paunching

I like to pinch the skin of the abdomen between the back legs and make a small incision with a sharp knife avoiding the gut, then insert both fore fingers into the abdomen which is then split (there appears to be a natural seam) down to within 2·5 cm (1 in.) of the rib cage. Loosen the bladder (emptied before being hung up!) and rectum then loosen the lungs from the rib cage (a thin membrane separates the rib cage from the abdomen and this has to be broken) and the viscera should all fall out in one lump into the container below. Remove the gall bladder from the liver and avoid allowing the contents to touch the flesh if at all possible as it taints. Leave the heart and kidneys in the carcase. Descriptions have their

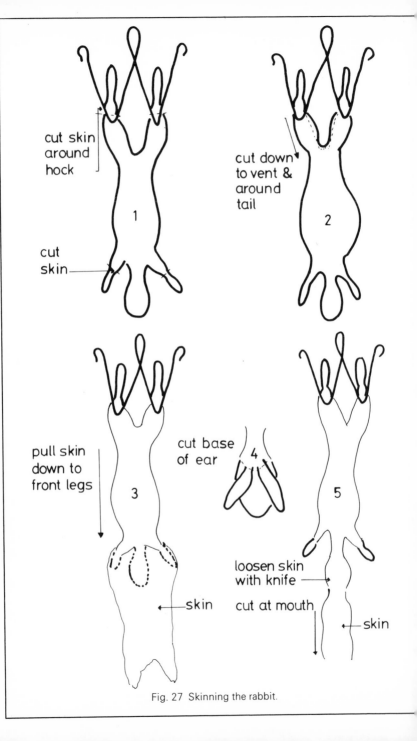

cut skin around hock

cut skin

1

cut down to vent & around tail

2

pull skin down to front legs

3

cut base of ear

4

5

loosen skin with knife

cut at mouth

skin

skin

Fig. 27 Skinning the rabbit.

limitations but the best way is to watch an experienced operator if at all possible. They can often be found lurking in the bars of country pubs. The carcase may now be removed from the nail or hook and taken indoors to be jointed—see Figure 29. Cool in the refrigerator and cook after twenty-four hours. Cooked immediately after skinning, the flesh is a bit gelatinous. The guts must be disposed of before the flies are attracted to them. Dogs will dig really deeply to unearth buried viscera, so wrap them in several thicknesses of paper before disposal if you do not want all the dogs of the neighbourhood around.

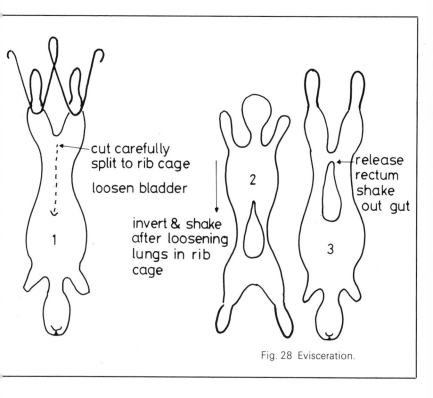

cut carefully
split to rib cage

loosen bladder

invert & shake
after loosening
lungs in rib
cage

1

2

release
rectum
shake
out gut

3

Fig. 28 Evisceration.

Cooking rabbit meat

The domestic deep freeze has meant that the glut of produce from meat, fruit, vegetables and cakes can be stored for later use. Always joint the rabbit before freezing. Cool the jointed rabbit in a refrigerator after packaging in meal-sized quantities, each joint wrapped separately in clingwrap film in *flat* packs (this assists rapid freezing). Foil or plastic trays are ideal for this. The whole is then put in an airtight plastic bag, the air sucked out, the bag secured with freezer tape or wire ties and *labelled* with number and name of joints, date and year. This will keep at least eight months if stored at −20 degrees centigrade.

When thawing take out the required pack and place in the refrigerator for at least twenty-four hours; rapid thawing may spoil the texture of the meat. Some people have found that deep-frozen rabbit meat does not fry as well as fresh, but I have not found this to be so.

I have included a few basic recipes which with a little ingenuity can be adapted and improved with the aid of the individual cook's imagination.

Prime young rabbit meat can be prepared in a variety of ways from methods requiring a short cooking time to stewing or marinating for long periods. Old rabbit or one of indeterminate age will benefit from a long period of slow cooking to soften the fibres. Generally the more mature the rabbit the better the basic flavour, but the young rabbit will win on its fine texture and juiciness.

Wild rabbit is traditionally soaked in salt water for several hours after jointing to help ameliorate its tendency to strong flavour. This is not necessary with homegrown table-rabbit meat. An old boiler may improve with hanging for three or four days in winter before cooking.

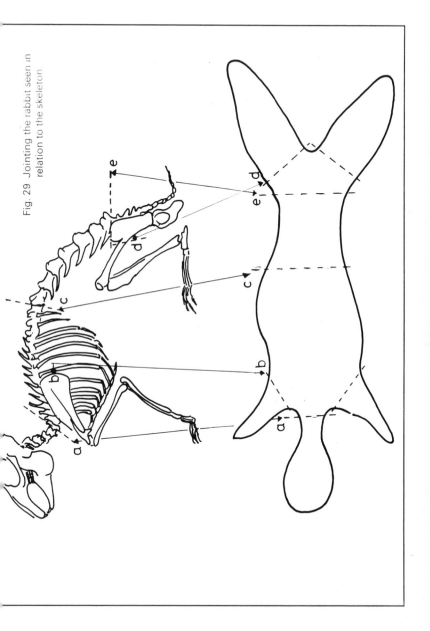

Fig. 29 Jointing the rabbit seen in relation to the skeleton.

Recipes

(These recipes are scaled to 25 g to each ounce, which is recommended by the Metrication Board for cooking purposes.)

Fried young rabbit

2 tablespoons plain flour
seasoning
1 large egg
125 ml ($\frac{1}{4}$ pint) milk

All the joints except the rib cage and head can be utilised here.

Coat joints in plain flour seasoned with a little salt, pepper and any flavouring you particularly like.

Dip into batter made with flour, egg and milk.

Fry in shallow or deep fat taking care to reduce the heat after first 30 seconds. Gently fry for 15 minutes, depending on size of joints. Serve with fresh lettuce, salad and mashed potato.

Sweet sour rabbit

250 ml ($\frac{1}{2}$ pint) wine vinegar
2–3 sticks celery
small tin of tomatoes
a few capers
4 tablespoons moist dark brown sugar

Joint rabbit and wipe clean.

Dip in seasoned flour, lightly fry till golden brown in butter in frying pan.

Place joints in casserole with other ingredients.

Cover and bake in moderate oven 325°F (160°C) gas mark 3 for $1\frac{1}{2}$–2 hours.

Curried rabbit

1 jointed rabbit
50 g (2 oz) butter
Sauce one chopped onion

1 dessertspoon flour
1 tablespoon curry powder
1 chicken bouillon cube or chicken Oxo cube
375 ml ($\frac{3}{4}$ pint) water
1 cooking apple
1 dessertspoon Indian mango chutney
1 tablespoon marmalade
25 g (1 oz) sultanas
25 g chopped nuts—blanched almonds
1 tablespoon brown sugar
cream or milk to taste

Lightly fry joints in butter in saucepan.
Remove and drain.
Fry chopped onion and apple in butter over low heat till soft but not brown.
Add flour, curry powder, stir continuously over low heat 3–4 minutes.
Stir in water and stock cube.
Add remaining ingredients including rabbit.
Simmer in covered pan for $1\frac{1}{2}$ hours.
Remove meat from bone when flesh is tender.
Transfer meat to casserole, cover with curry sauce and add cream or milk.
Serve with long grain rice and usual curry accompaniments.

Rabbit pâté

400 g (1 lb) boneless rabbit
200 g ($\frac{1}{2}$ lb) belly pork
50 g (2 oz) peeled onion
1 tablespoon sherry or brandy
pinch of thyme
2 tablespoons chopped parsley
salt, freshground pepper
1 beaten egg
100 g (4 oz) thinly sliced streaky bacon (rind removed)
bay leaf

Mince rabbit, pork, and onion 2 or 3 times.
Add sherry, herbs, salt and pepper.
Stir in egg and mix well.
Line a 1½-pint earthenware dish with bacon, pack in mixture and cover with foil.
Bake 1½ hours 177°C (320°F) gas mark 4.
Leave to mature in fridge for 2 days before eating.

Rabbit liver pâté

Liver
Butter
Salt and pepper
Nutmeg and mace
Drop or two of brandy (optional)
Weigh the liver and lightly fry it in half its weight in butter till cooked through
Pound cooked liver in a bowl with the butter, pepper and salt, pinch of nutmeg, pinch of mace.
Press through hair or nylon sieve.
Add drop or two of brandy.
Press into small jar and cover with fresh melted butter.
Excellent on thin toast as a starter or as sandwich filling.

Rabbit stew

Jointed rabbit including head (remove eyes, without breaking them, by loosening with forefinger then cutting loose with sharp knife). Soak in salt water for an hour or so if rabbit is elderly.
3 carrots
2 sticks celery
1 chopped onion
beef stock
Coat rabbit in seasoned flour, gently brown in butter in frying pan.
Put in casserole.

Sweat chopped onion in frying pan for 5 minutes.
Add onion and remaining vegetables to casserole.
Cover with beef stock and bake till tender at 325°F
(160°C) gas mark 3. The longer it is cooked the better
the flavour. The head can be utilised in this recipe.
Cook whole. Especially succulent are the cheeks and
tongue. The brains are eaten with a salt spoon by the
youngest member of the family. These can be exposed
by inserting a sharp knife in the middle of the skull
and cracking it open.

Rabbit pie
Small pack frozen flaky pastry
one jointed rabbit
100 g (4 oz) end pieces of bacon
dripping
2 sliced onions
250 ml ($\frac{1}{2}$ pint) stock
salt and pepper
Fry rabbit and chopped bacon in dripping, add onion.
Season, add stock and simmer till tender.
Cool. Take meat off bone.
Fill pie dish with meat, bacon, onion and stock.
Cover with pastry.
Cook $\frac{3}{4}$ hour 370°F (190°C) gas mark 5 till golden
brown.

Fricasee of rabbit
1 jointed rabbit
1 onion
100 g ($\frac{1}{4}$ lb) mushrooms
bouquet garni
seasoning
50 g (2 oz) butter
50 g (2 oz) flour
250 ml ($\frac{1}{2}$ pint) milk
250 ml ($\frac{1}{2}$ pint) white stock (chicken Oxo cube)

squeeze of lemon juice

Put jointed rabbit in pan with onions, mushrooms, seasoning and stock.

Bring to boil, then simmer for 1 hour (till meat slips off bone).

Put pieces of meat on hot dish.

Strain liquor.

Melt butter in saucepan, add flour and cook for a minute, stirring constantly.

Add liquor, lemon juice and milk and continue stirring until it thickens. Pour over meat.

Garnish with bacon rolls, chopped parlsey and croutons.

Rabbitburgers

4 cups minced rabbit

1 teaspoon salt

$\frac{1}{2}$ teaspoon pepper

$\frac{1}{2}$ teaspoon sage

$\frac{1}{4}$ cup breadcrumbs

1 egg

$\frac{1}{2}$ onion

small bayleaf

$\frac{1}{4}$ cup milk

$\frac{1}{2}$ teaspoon paprika

Chop onion finely.

Beat egg well.

Mix all ingredients together thoroughly.

Divide into 12 and form into patties.

Coat in oatmeal, fry until cooked.

Rabbit special

Jointed rabbit

Marinade

375 ml ($\frac{3}{4}$ pint) cheap red wine

2 tablespoons chopped carrot and onion

1 tablespoon chopped parsley
bayleaf
3 cloves
black pepper
$\frac{1}{2}$ teaspoon salt

Sauce
50 g (2 oz) lard
50 g (2 oz) bacon diced
75 g (3 oz) chopped onion
Beef stock
1 tablespoon sugar
75 g (3 oz) wine vinegar
50 g (2 oz) sultanas
50 g (2 oz) chopped almonds
salt, pepper, lemon juice
100 g (4 oz) bitter chocolate
Soak rabbit in marinade for 4 hours.
Drain and dry.
Roll in seasoned flour.
Brown in lard with bacon and onion.
Strain marinade over rabbit, add beef stock and simmer for $1\frac{1}{2}$ hours.
Caramelise sugar in *thick* saucepan, then add vinegar, salt, pepper and lemon juice and stir.
Pour over meat.
Add sultanas, nuts, grated bitter chocolate.
Serve and savour the result.

Pelts

The skins of rabbits to be used for pelts *must* come from a reasonably mature animal. The fur should be in prime condition and this is most likely at about Christmas time. Moulting must have been fully completed before killing or dark marks will show on the skin where the moult was still in progress. The order of moulting is generally neck, flanks and rump, and then the belly, though there is no hard and fast rule. If the skinning has been done by the sleeve method the pelt will have to be cut down the abdomen to open it up, using a sawing motion with a very sharp knife. This wet skin is then carefully laid fur down on a stretching board about 70 × 50 cm (30 in. × 20 in.). The first four nails are vital and with experience one learns how far apart to place them at the four corners of the pelt *without over-stretching*. The filling-in nails need to be carefully placed as near to the edge of the skin as possible without tearing. Examine the skin the following day to ensure that the edges are flat. If necessary use a peg to flatten them out. The fat is then removed with a *blunt* knife together with any scraps of flesh, taking care not to scratch or damage the skin. The board is then hung out of the sunlight in a cool airy shed to dry. In summer a newspaper tacked over the skin will keep the flies away. Drying takes place remarkably quickly—in up to three days. Make sure that the skin is thoroughly dry before storing flat for selling. Lay the skins fur to fur and skin to skin in a box and store in an even temperature, the pelts having been dusted both sides with furrier's naphthalene. Look at the skins carefully at frequent intervals for weevils or any other infestation.

Home curing

This is a very skilled job and not to be recommended as time and materials can too easily be wasted. Ideally it is easier to practise on a newly flayed sheep skin as this is far thicker and more foolproof. These can easily be obtained from the local slaughter house for a small sum.

There are several methods varying in complication. The best way is to try the one that appeals to you best.

First method (for sheep first!). Soak freshly flayed skin

in rainwater for twenty-four hours (to remove blood), changing the water twice. Take out and scrape the skin with a blunt knife (or paint scraper for the sheep skin). Rub the skin with a salt solution made up from boiling 28 g (1 oz) of common salt with the same quantity of saltpetre in 0·57 of a litre (1 pint) of water. Rub this in every other day for a week. Don't nail it onto a board but dry the skin naturally in a cool airy shed, stretching it from time to time to prevent it from becoming stiff and from shrinking. When it feels reasonably dry, wash with Lux or other very milk soap and allow to dry naturally again. Rub the leather side back and forth over the back of a chair until it is thoroughly supple.

Another Method. Using equal parts saltpetre and powdered alum, obtainable from a chemist, rub the mixture well into the defatted fresh skin. Leave for a day fur down in a fly-free area where it will stiffen. Work over back of a chair leather side down pulling it all ways. Wash the supple skin in borax and water to clean it. Hang out to dry again, pulling it all ways at intervals to prevent shrinking and stiffening. *Remember*—a rabbit skin is very tender and thin.

Cured Paws and Tail. Not for the squeamish! After skinning the rabbit, immediately remove the front and hind paws cutting the foot side of the hock and knee joints. Ask your chemist to make up a 38 per cent to 40 per cent solution of formaldehyde; using a hypodermic needle inject 5 ml of the solution into the severed end of the foot withdrawing the needle slowly. Hang the feet to dry in the inevitable cool airy place for only two to three weeks. Formaldehyde is poisonous so *do* keep it out of the way of children and pets. As a precaution, use rubber gloves when doing this and if any of the solution *does* get on the skin wash thoroughly with soap and water. After the drying has been completed the article is safe. The tails will obviously need far less formaldehyde. These are often used by horticulturalists as pollinators. The paws are incorporated into brooches, key-rings etc.

Angora fur

The angora rabbit is the only breed from which fur for spinning can be obtained. As well as the white-furred variety there are brown, blue, golden and smoke-coloured rabbits.

This rabbit matures at about 2·75 kg (or 6 lb) and is plucked or clipped several times a year yielding from 113 to 450 g (4 oz to 1 lb) of fur. This wool crop is greatly enhanced by intensive feeding. A well-grown intensively fed Angora can be cropped as early as eight weeks. Plucking must be done *extremely gently* over several days (as the skin of the rabbit is very tender), much as one would pluck a fowl. On the other hand they can be clipped with scissors. This breed must be regularly groomed with a baby's hair brush (at least daily) or the fur, being so fine, will quickly become irretrievably matted. It is inadvisable to keep the breed on a wooden floor covered with straw as the litter quickly becomes entangled in the very fine wool. A mesh floor is usually employed, keeping a sharp lookout for possible sore hocks. Hay must be fed from a well-constructed hay rack to prevent too much falling to the ground.

7 Health in the Rabbitry

Some of us *think* we know the look of a healthy rabbit. An impression of sparkling coat with bright eyes is often taken as the sure sign of health. However, it is a good idea to train oneself to *develop* this ability to judge the health of our animals. This is probably one of the most important facets of good stockmanship.

The head

The *ears* in the healthy rabbit will be continuously moving independently one way or another to catch any strange sound that may foretell danger. At rest the animal's ears may lie along its back. However, the healthy Lop rabbit's broad ears hang down naturally. The sound rabbit's ears have perfectly clean silky-textured hair on the outside. The inside of the ear appears hairless but on looking closer, one notices a few slightly coarser hairs which help prevent the entry of foreign bodies. The skin has a shiny appearance and should be perfectly clean and free from excessive grease, dirt or encrustations of scab or loose dead skin. Ears that are very cold to the touch may indicate that the animal is chilled. Excessively hot conditions may cause the ears to become pinker and feel hot. The normal condition is a natural warmth. The eye of a healthy rabbit radiates health. It is bright, with a complete lack of discharge. The rabbit gives the impression of never blinking, but actually it blinks so fast as not to be noticed. Beside the upper and lower lids, which both have eyelashes, there is a third fleshy pink lid known as the nictitating membrane, which appears from the side of the eye nearest the nose and covers the eyeball under the other lids. This membrane may well be drawn halfway across the eye if the animal is frightened. The lid is retracted once more when normal conditions are resumed. An excessively bright eye may indicate a high temperature. The *nose* is continually and rhythmically twitching and thereby exposes an extremely sensitive area (which is able to detect a wide range of scents). Two hairy folds of skin overlap the normally concealed nostrils which lie in the groove which is hairless. The nose showing any sign of discharge indicates ill health. The *mouth* is normally closed in repose, the sensitive lips being covered with short fine hairs. These hairs should be dry and clean. The upper lip is divided, enabling the animal to nibble very close to the ground.

The body

The *coat* of the animal varies in length with the breed. From the long, soft, silky hair of the Angora, up to 15 cm (6 in.) or more, to the normal-haired breeds, we come to the Rex coated breeds where the fur feels much like that of the mole. The normal furred rabbit has guard hairs (similar to those on the coat of the wild rabbit) which are longer and slightly coarser than those of the undercoat. The over-all impression of the healthy rabbit's coat is an almost oily sheen with no hint of scurf from the skin apparent.

Being born almost hairless, the rabbit rapidly grows its soft nest coat. This in turn is replaced by the intermediate coat, starting at about six weeks. Depending on the breed, the final adult and 'tight' coat is apparent at about six months. In order to maintain full protective warmth, most rabbits subsequently have a moult once a year. The moult is the normal process of shedding old hair and replacing it with new. The new coat grows as the old coat goes. It

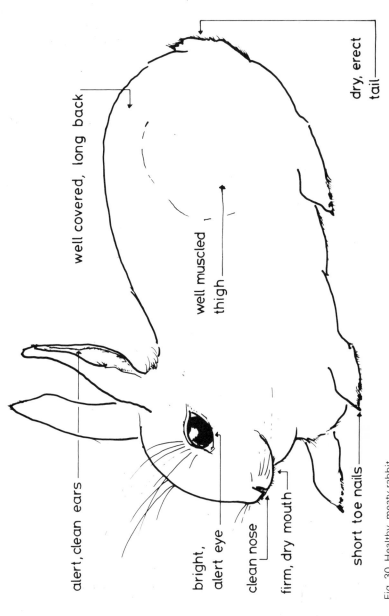

dry, erect tail

well covered, long back

well muscled thigh

alert, clean ears

bright, alert eye

clean nose

firm, dry mouth

short toe nails

Fig. 30 Healthy, meaty rabbit.

III

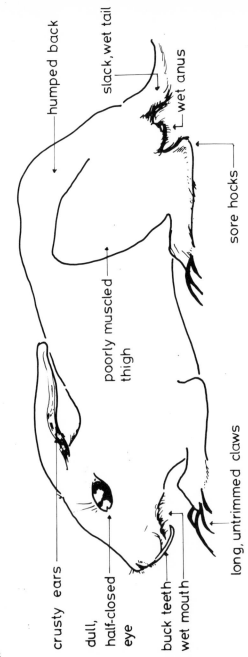

humped back

slack, wet tail

wet anus

sore hocks

poorly muscled thigh

crusty ears

dull, half-closed eye

buck teeth

wet mouth

long, untrimmed claws

Fig. 31 Unhealthy, poor type of rabbit.

is best to avoid mating at this time as the rabbit's food intake will be needed for the replacement of the fur, and the added strain of carrying young may result in small litters. The moult often starts on the head when first indications will be seen as loose hair on the top of the head between the eyes. The moult then moves along the back to the flanks and belly. The speed of moult is a factor which can be bred for. The quality and length of hair can be improved by good feeding. As hair is largely protein, a high level of nutrition will help to speed the growth of the new coat. The speed of moult is often quicker in hot weather than in the winter months. To tell if the moult is complete, blow the fur and dark patches can clearly be seen on the skin when the moult is still in progress. The *tail* is normally held upwards close to the rump and is covered with fine fluffy hair underneath with smoother-textured hair on top. The under parts of the tail may be a good indication of health, as hair stained by faeces or urine will indicate that there may be some digestive disorder or disease present. A normally healthy rabbit frequently washes its fur from the ears to the tail which accounts for its sweet, clean smell. The *hind legs* of the rabbit should be strong and well muscled and able to support the weight of the body. The hocks must be well furred to prevent soreness (see page 127) and withstand the natural instinct of the rabbit to stamp. The adults are quick to thump when startled, and this in turn warns the young to be alert. The male and female will also often stamp during mating. The paw has five toes with claws which grow continuously. The wild rabbit's claws are worn down by hopping about and scratching the soil to make burrows. Unless the claws are frequently observed and trimmed (see page 127), the animal can be lamed by their excessive length or may damage others when fighting or mating. An overlong claw may get ripped off by accident. The normal action in the rabbit is to hop, though the nestling will walk when it first emerges from the nest. It soon learns to hop in the characteristic mannner.

Attitude

Having noted all the physical characteristics of the healthy rabbit, the good stockman is able to further judge the health of the animal from its general demeanour. The robust animal is normally active and interested in what is going on around its hutch. The ears are continually moving, eyes bright and nose continually twitching. The healthy animal shows great interest when its feeder is heard. At such times it may jump up on its hind legs and put its paws on the door. The animal to watch is the one which shows little or no interest when fresh food is offered. This rabbit *could* be dead by the next feed. The healthy rabbit has a streamlined look about it where the unfit one has a hunched appearance. The flesh is firm and full on either side of the backbone with an impression of elasticity when the skin is gently felt. The sickening rabbit, however, feels stringy and mean across the back with possibly a prominent backbone. The skin feels tight and unresisting.

Respiration

This is normally barely perceptible in the adult rabbit at rest. If watched very carefully it will be noticed that the respiration rate is about 45 to 60 ventilations per minute. This is often difficult to observe as the rabbit may hop off, so it is easier to count the respirations for half a minute and double the figure to get a rough estimate for the minute rate. Young nestlings, however, are far easier to estimate as while still in the nest the body heaves quite obviously when breathing and the normal rate may be 80 to 100 per minute.

Whilst excited or under stress, the rate of respiration may rise alarmingly but will return to normal soon after the stimulation has ceased. This reaction will not occur when the animal is suffering from pneumonia (see page 119) when the rate may reach 130 or more per minute and be painfully obvious as the whole animal heaves in its effort to breathe. In this case the actual breathing process will be heard plainly and may be accompanied by bubbling noises from the throat.

Excretion

The urine of the rabbit normally consists of a yellowish-brown clear or *slightly* cloudy fluid. The healthy rabbit usually uses one corner of the hutch to the exclusion of all others. Any departure from this colour or behaviour must be suspect. A reddish hue can indicate kidney trouble. The smell is normally rabbity with a very slight suggestion of ammonia. Strong ammonia fumes will indicate a lack of thorough and frequent cleaning of hutches, poor ventilation, over-crowding, incorrect feeding or even possibly too much dandelion being fed (this plant is a well-known diuretic).

The droppings take the form of two types of pellets; the well-known oval dry or fawn-brown type seen in certain areas frequented by wild rabbits are most common. The pellet will be firm and fairly smooth to the touch, but obviously made up of well-digested pieces of fibre. The other kind is the coprophagous type (see page 64) which are often smaller, possibly slightly longer and rather mucoid, smooth and brown. Most rabbits will deposit these in the urinating area. Any departure from the norm in colour, smell, texture and shape may indicate disease. The *smell* of the rabbitry is a very good indication of the health of its inmates. A normal animal smell is acceptable. A sour, sickly or bad smell indicates all is not well. A good time to judge *smell* is in the dark when one's senses are less likely to be sidetracked by what one *sees*, or in the morning when the hutches are first opened.

Feeding behaviour

An accurate assessment of the animal's health can be its attitude towards its food. Fresh food is eagerly sought after by the robust rabbit. The ailing animal may huddle in a corner when offered fresh food. Water consumption can be measured when offered in individual drinking bottles or bowls. An automatic device will give no indication of quantities taken. The male or empty female, if fed a pelleted ration, may drink about 0·25 litres (half a pint) where a doe with a six-week-old litter of six to eight young may drink more than 2 litres (3 pints). When fed a diet of mainly green stuff, water intake will be greatly reduced. Of course, the weather conditions and temperature will affect water intake as well. Where the unfit animal crouches over the drinker, enteritis (see page 118) must be suspected.

Your veterinary surgeon

Some veterinary practices with more than one partner may have a specialist in small animals. In other practices each vet will be expected to treat all comers from horses to mice. It is advisable to find your nearest suitable vet *before* he or she may be needed. Keep a record of his telephone number and surgery times in a prominent place. It is expensive to call a vet to your own premises. It is cheaper to take the animal to the surgery if at all possible, where more extensive facilities will be available.

To cut down the risk of cross-infection, take the animal in a disposable box which can be burnt after use. A strong cardboard box lined with plastic (to prevent possible puddles in the surgery) and some soft litter is suitable, choosing the size to suit the animal. Choose a box small enough to prevent the animal struggling or falling about, yet sufficiently large for it to sit comfortably. A few air holes cut in the top and some strong string will complete the picture.

Be prepared to tell the vet as succinctly as possible the age of the animal, any unusual behaviour you may have noticed, the type of food it has been receiving and the state of its appetite. A sample of its droppings may also be helpful.

Post-mortem examination

A veterinary surgeon will perform a post-mortem on a rabbit which dies from an unknown cause. When delivering the animal to the surgery for post-mortem *mark it clearly* with your name, address and any relevant information such as age, diet, symptoms before death. Try to get the body to the surgery as soon as possible after death and remember to tell the attendant of its arrival.

Conditions which can lead to death:

Coccidiosis

Possible symptoms : Diarrhoea
                           Listlessness
                           Emaciation
                           Prominent backbone
                           Failure to feed
                           Nestlings dying

Coccidiosis is caused by a protozoan.

Preventive Action. As the disease is transmissible by rabbits eating food infected by the droppings of infected animals, strict attention must be paid to cleanliness of troughs and drinkers which may become foul, and avoiding the placement of food on the floor. Nest boxes and hutches must be thoroughly scrubbed and disinfected between litters. Avoid collecting green stuff from areas known to be used by wild rabbits. Don't pick green stuff growing near a fresh rabbit manure heap.

Treatment. Most pelleted rations contain an anti-coccidiosis drug which may prevent a serious outbreak if the hygiene of the rabbitry is good. The presence of such a coccidiostat will be clearly stated on the pellet bag. Animals fed a non-medicated pellet or an extensive diet of green stuff, hay and 'straights' may be treated with Embazin. Mix 10 ml with one litre of water (5 fluid ounces to 3 gallons of water) for six days. Allow the rabbits no other fluid than the medicated water and feed as dry and palatable a diet as possible to encourage drinking. However, rabbits which carry the organism may show no signs of the disease. A state of 'premunity' can exist—a balance between organism and host. Anything that weakens the host and upsets the balance in favour of the parasite, e.g. dietary change, chilling, other disease etc, can result in an upsurge of the disease.

Enteritis

The good stockman will be fully acquainted with the size and form of the droppings being produced by each group of rabbits. Any change in form of the faeces combined with an unpleasant smell not usually associated with the rabbits must immediately put the stockman on his guard. This condition is caused by irritation of the digestive organs which in turn can predispose the animal to other diseases, e.g. Coccidiosis.

Possible symptoms : Loss of appetite
Constant drinking and grinding of teeth

Diarrhoea
Wet fur round anus
Pot belly accompanied by audible
grumbling in gut

Preventive Action. Cut down areas of stress in management. If the type of feeding must be changed, do so gradually. If feeding intensively, check age of pellets. (When in doubt contact your supplier and quote the serial number of the bags). Check that none of the food is mouldy or musty. If feeding extensively avoid feeding frozen green stuff. Ensure that a wide variety of greenery is fed and don't be tempted to feed an entire meal of one species, e.g. clover. Always have hay available. Regular feeding times help reduce the chance of gorging with the resultant digestive upset and scouring.

Treatment. Don't remove the water in an attempt to cut down the loss of fluid as the rabbit will become dehydrated. Animals obviously severely distressed and dehydrated are best killed. Animals less severely affected, still active and feeding, can be offered blackberry leaves or groundsel (available all the year round), shepherd's purse, chickweed and oak leaves. Comfrey, available from April to October, is ideal for weaning rabbits, and it is an excellent food and does not predispose to enteritis. If *many* rabbits are affected contact the vet. However, the domestic unit can usually control the condition by offering the suggested wild plants, one or more of which will generally clear this complaint.

Pneumonia
Faulty ventilation in the rabbitry causing draughts, fluctuating temperatures and high humidity resulting from damp conditions, all give ideal situations for the development of pneumonia. The experienced stock-

man immediately knows the atmosphere in which he may find rabbits suffering from this complaint. This is not likely to be found in outdoor hutches.

Possible Symptoms. Huddled rabbits, rapid breathing requiring effort, bubbling in throats and noses (see page 115) may be heard, no appetite, and watery discharge from the eyes and noses. Death is usually very rapid, so dead rabbits may be the first sign of the disease.

Preventive Action. Check all ventilation until conditions in rabbitry feel healthy and pleasant. Avoid draughts with nestlings and weanlings. Feed good rations.

Treatment. Cull all affected stock. Veterinary treatment not economic in this case.

Myxomatosis

This is a virus disease introduced from Australia in 1954. It rapidly spread from the southern counties of England killing thousands of wild rabbits. It is now endemic and generally appears in the late summer or autumn when the wild rabbit population is at its greatest. The virus is spread by rabbit fleas and possibly mosquitoes and other biting insects.

Possible Symptoms. Swelling of all orifices, eyes, ears, mouth and external sexual organs. Listlessness leading to complete inactivity and eventual death.

Preventive Action. Don't gather wild food from areas known to be frequented by wild rabbits. Prevent pets, cats and dogs, which may have caught fleas from infected wild rabbits, from gaining access to rabbit hutches. Build manure heaps (where flies may breed) away from the rabbitry. Cover vent openings of rabbitry with fine mesh to keep out biting insects.

Cooper's dairy insect spray can be used safely around hutches to combat insects in hot weather.

Treatment. Kill all victims *as soon* as the disease is noticed and *burn*. Vaccination is available from Mansai Laboratories Ltd, Herons Way, Wey Road, Weybridge, Surrey. Tel. No. 45354. This will give protection for nine months when a booster dose will be required.

Snuffles
This can be caused mechanically by dusty food, litter and general conditions. Infectious colds come under this heading.

Possible Symptoms. The rabbit irritated by dust will sneeze and possibly discharge mucus from nose and eyes. Prolonged irritation will predispose the animal to other infections of the respiratory tract. Colds will cause the animal to sneeze and wipe its nose with its front paws, thus wet front paws may be a sign of snuffles.

Preventive Action. Avoid dusty litters by using self-dusting hoppers. If bowls are used for pellets see that they are emptied of any dust regularly. Avoid dusty hay by good making, or buying and storing in suitable conditions (see page 64). Ensure adequate ventilation and avoid draughts. Don't overcrowd.

Treatment. Remove the cause of irritation, e.g. hay, dust, and this may effect a cure. The discharge from the nose caused by colds is extremely infectious and any suspect animal is best immediately isolated until the cause is known. If the disease is obviously infectious, the infected animals are best culled. A mild discharge may be alleviated by holding eucalyptus on a pad of cotton wool in front of the nose.

Disorders in breeding stock:

Mastitis
This condition may be encountered in lactating animals.

Possible Symptoms. Rabbits huddled, lack of appetite in extreme cases, the mammary glands obviously congested, lumpy, red and painful.

Preventive Action. Ensure good management which may allow doe to produce enough strong healthy stock to suck from all available teats. Cull any doe which has mastitis in two succeeding litters. Avoid any sharp areas which could cause scratches to mammary glands resulting in bacterial infections. Ensure nest entrance is the correct height to avoid damage to teats. Have adequate palatable rations to encourage nestlings to feed early. This reduces stimulation of the doe which will naturally reduce the milk output before the young are removed at weaning. See that general hygiene is good. Don't foster litters from affected does.

Treatment. A warm cloth applied to swollen glands will help relieve the congestion. In extreme cases gentle expression of the milk will help. A teaspoonful of salt dissolved in $\frac{1}{2}$ litre (1 pint) of warm water can be used to bathe the congested area several times a day and this will reduce the swelling. This is best made fresh daily. The veterinary surgeon may recommend antibiotic treatment in stubborn cases.

Vent disease
This is often associated with damp and dirty conditions. Any obvious discharge from the sexual organs of either buck or doe must preclude further

mating until the disorder is cleared as it may be extremely catching. Your veterinary surgeon will advise you on treatment.

Abortion
Dead embryo rabbits found littered round the hutch would indicate that the doe has aborted.

Preventive Action. Limit handling of the in kindle doe to the very minimum especially with the highly strung animals. However, if the young doe is handled frequently before she is mated she is less likely to be upset by any essential handling during pregnancy. Select does with a calm temperament. Avoid noisy surroundings. Ensure nest box entrance is correct size and height for the rabbit to avoid bruising. Records outside each doe's hutch must indicate date of mating and expected dates of kindling. Excessively bright lights over hutches of in kindle does is best avoided as it may stimulate early kindling resulting in stillbirths.

Treatment. A doe which aborts more than once should be culled. Don't be tempted to use the doe which has aborted to foster young from another litter. She may be suffering from an infectious disease.

Sterility

Preventive Action. Adequate good feeding, but avoid overfeeding in both buck and doe. Don't allow too long a period to elapse before mating after the young have been weaned. Don't overwork the buck. Calmness on the part of the handler during mating is essential. Sufficient light available up to sixteen hours a day for does but avoid excessive bright lights for bucks. Breed from a known stock of proven breeding ability.

Parasites:

External

Canker of the Ear. This is caused by a mite which is barely visible to the naked eye. The presence of these mites causes intense irritation which makes the rabbit shake its head and scratch its ears, increasing the inflammation. The crusty scabs caused by the mite are thus spread around the hutch. The mite can survive up to four weeks without a host so careful disinfection of all hutches is essential.

Treatment. This is one of the few rabbit complaints which need not precipitate culling. Clean the scabs and crustiness from the ear cavity gently with cotton wool soaked in olive oil. Apply B.H.C. emulsion or a proprietary dust available from your veterinary surgeon. Burn all litter from hutches.

Mange. This is not common but rabbits can be affected by sarcoptic mange. This is caused by a minute mite which burrows in the pores of the skin causing *intense* irritation. Obtain a suitable preparation from the vet and bathe the animal thoroughly according to instructions. This infection is extremely contagious and can be caught by humans. The animal is best destroyed, the litter burnt and the hutch thoroughly disinfected with remaining wash. The infected animal if left untreated will eventually become emaciated through the extreme irritation which prevents feeding.

Fleas. As we have seen, the fleas transmitted from wild rabbits to tame ones can carry myxomatosis. Keep pets out of the rabbitry and away from hutches. Dusting with I.C.I. flea powder, paying particular attention to the ears, will kill any fleas present. Scratching and irritation caused by the presence of fleas may cause infertility in both bucks and does. It will also spoil any skins destined for pelts.

Internal

Worms are not now normally a problem, especially in the domestic rabbitry. If the presence of worms is suspected, a labelled sample of faeces can be taken from the suspected stock and the veterinary surgeon will diagnose and recommend the appropriate treatment.

The *tapeworm* is the most likely type to be found where dogs are kept. The adult tapeworm lives in the intestines of the dog, the eggs are voided and may fall on greenery which is subsequently fed to the rabbits and this forms cysts in the abdominal cavity of the rabbit or in the muscle tissues. These won't harm the animal unless growing on a vital part of the body. Nothing is seen in the rabbit's droppings.

General disorders:

Malocclusion of the teeth

The rabbit's teeth grow continually. Normally the upper and lower incisors meet with the uppers overlapping the lowers slightly and when the rabbit nibbles its food the biting surfaces are continually worn down.

Occasionally the upper and lower incisors do not meet and are thus not worn down. By eight weeks of age this deformity will be apparent and the animal may have grown tusks which will eventually prevent proper eating. These tusks can be clipped off with nail clippers or wire cutters but the kindest thing is to cull the animal. Take great care to check the animal's records because this is an inherited deformity and the

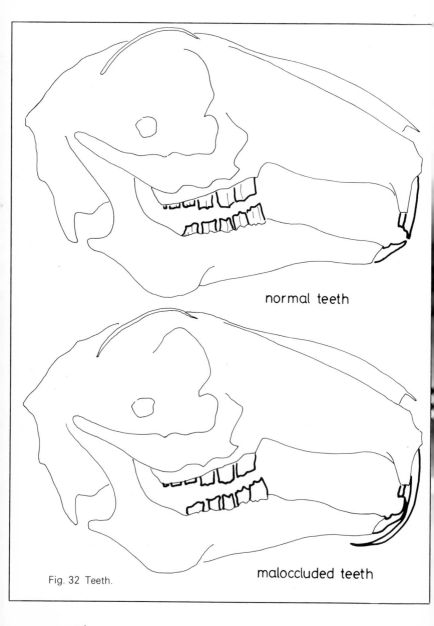

normal teeth

maloccluded teeth

Fig. 32 Teeth.

parents are best culled. An apparently normal rabbit can pass on this deformity if mated with one of similar tendency. Watch out for the broken opposite tooth not providing a wearing surface.

Normal teeth can be kept naturally trimmed by allowing access to hard cabbage stalks and twigs from trees. This may also prevent gnawing of hutches.

Wry neck

The rabbit which holds its head to one side may well be suffering from canker of the ear (see page 124). Penetration and subsequent inflammation of the inner ear, where the balancing organs are situated, will cause the rabbit to roll or teeter about. The affected animal is best culled.

Sore hocks

The rabbit's natural disposition to stamp may cause it to suffer from sore hocks which may in turn affect fertility as the discomfort involved can prevent mating. Does affected may not feed or tend their young as efficiently as they could.

Rabbits kept on a well-littered dry floor will seldom suffer. It is more often found in nervous stock kept on wire floors etc. Poorly furred or short-furred stock, e.g. the Rex breeds, are most likely to suffer. If it does occur, even in ideal surroundings, the badly affected animal is best culled. The under surfaces of the back legs become raw and then possibly infected. The infected areas can be cleaned with antiseptic ointment and dressed with an astringent ointment. A sock holding a bandage over the infected pad is seldom effective as the rabbit will not rest until it has rubbed off the bandage.

Long toe nails

This is another condition caused by the animal's

natural activities not being allowed free range. In the unnatural surroundings of the hutch the claws may soon grow overlong and will need trimming regularly. Cut the nail to 3–4 mm (1/6th to 1/7th of an inch) from the quick with nail clippers. The quick will be readily seen as the dark red area within the nail. It is difficult to say how often this will require to be done as different stock grow claws at different rates. A good plan is always check claw length each time the animal is handled.

As we have seen, it is clearly difficult to diagnose disease in the rabbit as so many disorders are inter-related. The plan is to have as high a level of management as possible to prevent the chance of any disorders occurring. Good stockmanship is natural to some but can be learnt by all. Sharp observation and a good nose kept continually on the lookout when handling stock or food will prevent most disorders.

Quarantine

The importance of quarantine quarters cannot be over-emphasised. Newly bought stock *must* be kept for at least four weeks in a different house or hutches well away from the main area. If possible wear a special coat when feeding the quarantine stock and leave the coat with them. Ideally one person should care for them alone. Failing this, feed your own stock first and then, after washing, feed the quarantine stock.

Very carefully observe the stock for health before bringing them into your own hutches. Check general health signs (see page 109) and for external parasites. If in any doubt get a second opinion from a knowledgeable friend.

Accident

Broken Limbs. The animal who suffers a broken limb is best destroyed. Rabbits are poor patients and rarely recover their former glory after a break. Obviously a favourite pet will deserve all the time its owner can bestow on it, but veterinary treatment is expensive and time-consuming.

Bleeding. When blood is noticed, immediately try to find the source. A mild wound caused by fighting or protruding ill-fitting equipment is best washed then dressed with an antiseptic anti-insect powder obtained from the vet. Large tears of flesh needing sewing are best dealt with by destroying the animal. The treatment is time-consuming and very expensive. Remove the offending bullying rabbit or protruding equipment to prevent a repeat performance.

Eyes

A foreign body will cause irritation to the eyes. The most likely cause will be dusty litter and pellets or an oat flight adhering to the surface. Golden eye ointment obtainable from the chemist can be squeezed into the corner of the eye. The eye is then held closed for a moment to allow the ointment to disperse.

Medicine chest

Golden eye ointment, cotton wool, scissors, antiseptic ointment, antiseptic dusting powder, nail clippers, T.C.P., coccidiosis treatment (embazin) and B.H.C. dusting powder.

Fig. 33 Dosing the rabbit. Wrap rabbit in towel; gently prise mouth open and insert gag stick; pour medicine down throat with spoon and massage throat to aid swallowing.

8 General Management

Identification of rabbits

The good stockman prides himself on his ability to distinguish each individual rabbit. On a domestic scale this will be reasonably easy. However, there will be times when quick identification is needed and this will be helped by some form of artificial marking.

Perhaps the easiest method is a small tag resembling a safety pin which is individually numbered and pinned into the rabbit's ear. This is *not foolproof*. It can easily be lost when torn out of the ear by accident. It is unsightly and unsuitable for exhibition stock. It is not recommended.

The British Rabbit Council sells *leg rings*. These are sold in nine different sizes according to the breed.

Each ring is numbered differently and when bought, the appropriate number is recorded against the name and address of the purchaser. When stock are sold, the appropriate number is transferred to the new owner and recorded at the British Rabbit Council (B.R.C.). This form of identification is used as a check at rabbit shows and exhibitions. The appropriate ring is placed on the back leg over the hock when the rabbit is about ten weeks old. It is large enough to still fit comfortably but not be removable by the time the animal is fullgrown.

Tattooing. This is employed by the commercial rabbitries. The inside ear is cleaned with surgical spirit to remove any grease. The tattoo punch is used to prick the ear with the appropriate identification and special tattooing ink is liberally rubbed into the prick marks.

Dyeing. Most farmers' sundriesmen stock dye sticks which are obtainable in different colours. However, the dye from these rapidly wears off. A cheaper and easier method is to use a *waterproof* fibretip marker. I have also used these on cattle and pigs. The colour will last up to six weeks. The added advantage is that these pens are available at most stationers.

Records
It is easy to imagine that we can keep a mental record of the production and food consumption of a small domestic rabbitry, especially when only a few does are kept and these are known individually. Memory is apt to play tricks and a successful method is to keep a few *simple* records.

Food Records. A record of all food bought, with date, can be kept on the wall above the food storage bins.

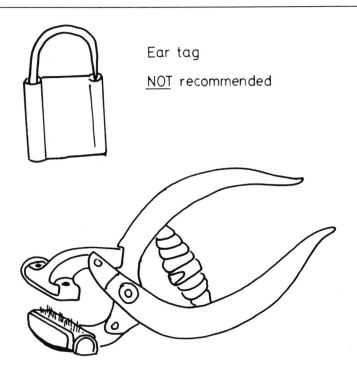

Ear tag

<u>NOT</u> recommended

Tattooing forceps. 1cm. size numbers

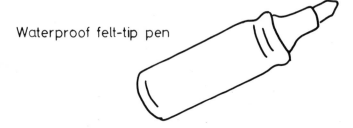

Waterproof felt-tip pen

Fig. 34 Methods of identification.

Breeding Records. A hutch card (attached but out of reach of the rabbits) can record mating dates, litter numbers and mortality. Remember to have a space for notes, these can cover observations on particular behaviour, faecal consistency etc, food consumption (e.g. daily rations), type of food and medication. The information from these cards can then be used for the selection of future breeding stock when assessing and comparing the performance of an individual animal.

Desk Diary. A desk dairy kept in a prominent place with pen or pencil firmly attached to record day-to-day observations will be found very helpful.

Having decided on the points which need to be recorded, devise the records as *simply* as possible and stick to them. For records to be of use they must be simply, easily and accurately kept up to date.

Temperature

A maximum–minimum thermometer is an interesting and even useful luxury. It can be hung in the rabbitry, or near the hutches of the animals if they are kept outside. A graph can be kept of the ambient temperature recorded morning and evening. This may help in the diagnosis of any disease outbreak.

Cleaning tools

Good hygiene is essential for the health of our rabbits. Simple efficient tools will help the thorough cleaning of the hutches. We have found that a *hoe* with a broken handle can easily be adapted for use as a scraper. Smooth the broken handle over with sandpaper or cut down to about 45 centimetres (18 in.). Bend the neck of the hoe so that the blade is at about an angle of 55 degrees to the handle. This will make scraping easier.

A *paint scraper* with a triangular head will prove

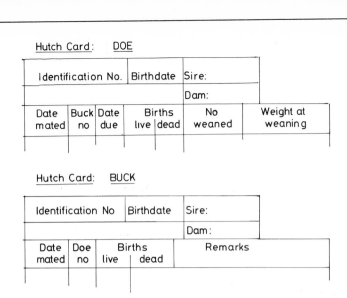

Hutch Card: DOE

Identification No.		Birthdate	Sire:	
			Dam:	

Date mated	Buck no	Date due	Births live	dead	No weaned	Weight at weaning

Hutch Card: BUCK

Identification No		Birthdate	Sire:
			Dam:

Date mated	Doe no	Births live	dead	Remarks

Feed Record Intensive

Date	Hutch No	Quantity	Remarks

Feed Record Extensive

Date	Hutch No	Type of food	Remarks

Telephone numbers

Service	Address	Exchange/std	Number
Vet			
Feed			

Fig. 35 Record cards.

useful for awkward and inaccessible corners.

A good-quality *scrubbing brush* is an essential. Kleeneze make a strong wooden-backed one with nylon bristles which seems to resist the temptation to go bald.

A *yard brush* can be used for sweeping up litter. Kleeneze make one with nylon bristles which with reasonable care will last for several years.

A *soft brush* with a long handle is essential for cobwebbing and removing dust from the rabbit shed.

A *wheelbarrow* is necessary for carting away manure. Try to scrub this each time it is used and use it only for manure. Clean litter can be carried on an open hemp sack with handles at the four corners.

A *stirrup pump* sometimes found at farm or country house sales will be ideal for spraying disinfectant.

Buckets for holding scrubbing water and soaking feeding and drinking utensils can be marked 'rabbit' to prevent their disappearance!

Cleaning and disinfection

Regular and frequent cleaning of all hutches is essential to the health of the rabbit, the exception being the lactating mother with young. I have found that if the doe's hutch is thoroughly cleaned a few days before kindling is due, she is then best left until the young are beginning to come out of the nest. This will help to avoid any upset which can result in the chilling of young and consequent disease, or even death. A good absorbent material for the urinating area is sawdust or even peat moss, and these materials can be covered with straw or hay. The type of litter used may be governed by the cost of the material. Sawdust can be obtained free for the collection in some areas, as can straw on occasions.

All other hutches will need to be cleaned regularly and more frequently to prevent litter becoming damp.

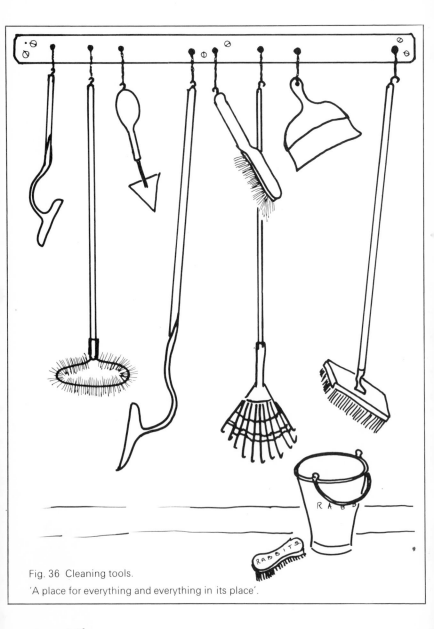

Fig. 36 Cleaning tools.

'A place for everything and everything in its place'.

Special attention must be paid to the buck's hutch in order to control strong ammonia fumes. Some like to move the occupant to a crate or spare hutch while cleaning out. However, it is usually possible to clean out the foul litter (scraping well into the corners) and to replace clean litter without too much difficulty while the occupants are present.

Between batches of fatteners the hutches must be cleaned more thoroughly. All litter is removed and the corners scraped thoroughly, paying particular attention to the walls and the roofs. The hutch is then thoroughly scrubbed with a suitable disinfectant following the maker's instructions (Jeyes' Fluid is suitable for use with animals). If possible, leave the hutch to dry in the sun. To help combat coccidiosis, a 1 per cent solution of ammonia can be sprayed inside the hutches. (This also has a remarkable effect on human colds I find, clearing a stuffy head very quickly!)

Resting hutches

There is not a lot known about this point apart from the fact that animals housed continually in the same building apparently fail to thrive as well as those housed in hutches which have been rested at intervals. Mortality rates in new hutches may be found to be lower than those experienced by rabbits housed in hutches which have been used continually for several years. Disposable nest boxes in breeding hutches help here. To combat this, wherever possible leave hutches empty between batches. Even a week's rest will help. Where outside Morant hutches are used in the summer the fattening hutches can be given a thorough spring-clean, disinfection, and subsequent rest until the autumn when the fatteners are housed in hutches once more.

Litter

Litter is used in all housing with the exception of wire cages housed in controlled-environment houses. It is required to absorb the inevitable moisture in the dung area and some materials even help as a deodoriser, e.g. peat moss and to a lesser extent sawdust. Litter also helps insulate the rabbits against extremes of temperature; some litter, e.g. hay and straw, acts as a deterrent to hutch-gnawing as it is sufficiently palatable for the animals to nibble.

Straw. Winter-sown straws are hard, spiky and unpalatable. Spring-sown wheat straw is only a little better. Spring-sown barley straw is generally the softest and the most palatable. Spring oat straw is liked by the rabbit but is not so soft. Bales vary *greatly* in weight but the average may be taken as 10 kg (25 lb).

Hay. This is expensive to use as litter especially if it is bought. In some seasons hay grown in the marshes is available at a comparatively low cost. Watch out for mustiness. If well made and cheap it may cost as little as a bale of good spring barley straw and is a better buy as it is palatable as well as more nutritious. It is not very absorbent and inclined to heat when damp.

Peat Moss. This is bought in bales of about 50 kg (1 cwt). It is expensive but a bale will last far longer than a bale of straw or hay. It can be dusty so watch out for the grade. It is inclined to stain the coats of the lighter-coloured breeds.

Sawdust. When collecting this, make sure it is dry and not excessively dusty. Generally fresh sawdust from newly felled trees is unsuitable as it sometimes heats thus forming musty lumps. Sawdust can often be obtained for a very small sum if collected from the sawmill. A hessian sugar-beet-pulp sack is suitable for carrying, carting and storing sawdust. Paper meal bags are not so good as the sawdust can't 'breathe'.

Paper. Shredded newspaper has been used in an emergency for litter.

Bracken. Bracken can be gathered free. However, the stems are extremely sharp when handled and it is advisable to use leather gloves when pulling it. It is best gathered after it has died down but make sure it is dry. Wet bracken quickly breaks down to a fine tilth more suitable as a possible compost than as litter!

Leaves. During the war I used dry leaves as litter and though they are not so absorbent as some litters, they *are* free. Leaves also contain plenty of entertainment value as the rabbits love rustling through them. However, they quickly break down into small pieces and will need constant renewal. Generally the leaves found in most deciduous woods are good, but avoid laurel leaves as they are poisonous in quantities. Gather the leaves when they are dry and store them in hessian sacks.

Earth and Ashes. These can be used in the dunging areas under the other litter. These materials are absorbent and deodorising but are very heavy when wet.

Manure

This leads us to manure. Even if there is no room for a garden there should be no difficulty in disposal of litter. Gardening neighbours will be delighted to remove the material. An acquaintance who keeps animals in her suburban backyard always has a queue of gardeners on cleaning-out days. Enthusiastic vegetable gardeners know its value as soil conditioner/moisture retainer and a source of plant nutrients. Rabbit manure can be used fresh on the soil but ideally it is best composted. Mark an area 2 m × 1·5 m (6 ft × 4 ft) (well away from the house and rabbitry) and build up the manure paying particular attention to the size of the heap. After each addition carefully tread the heap and cover with plastic to prevent excessive drying out in dry weather or the leaching out of the valuable nutrients by rain. The plastic cover also helps to maintain the heat generated by the breakdown of the manure. Continue to add manure until it reaches about 1·2 m (4 ft). If the heap feels dry when a hand is thrust inside, it will require turning sides to middle onto another patch, watering each layer with a watering can. If on the other hand the heap is soggy, turn it and incorporate some dry material, e.g. straw, leaves, garden waste; also add some *hydrated* lime to each layer. Cover with a layer of soil 10 cm (4 in.) deep and leave up to six months (depending on the prevailing weather conditions) for it to break down to form a smellfree valuable compost.

It is difficult to ascertain the actual quantities and composition of the manure produced by a rabbit, as it depends on the size, age and number of rabbits, also the method of littering (rabbits on wire floors will yield mere pellets!) The type of food will also affect the composition of the manure. Generally it can be said that weight for weight it is better value than farmyard manure. A dressing of 15 cm (6 in.) spread on the top of the soil in autumn will control weed growth and also be partly combined into the soil by the action of earthworms by the spring.

Rabbits give great pleasure from their birth to their ultimate demise whenever that might be. The secret of good stockmanship and also incidentally the greatly increased pleasure experienced by the owners, is to develop an inquisitive enquiring attitude to everything concerning the stock from the animals themselves, to their food and surroundings. *Really look* at everything with a fresh unbiased eye *always*. It is so easy to poke food and water at them twice daily and to change their litter without *really* looking at them. Try not to let any of the attentions bestowed on them become automatic and unseeing. Trouble can be nipped in the bud by the observant, caring owner. Attention and care bestowed on the animals will save time in the long run and experience will lend speed and efficiency.

Appendix I

Useful addresses

Ministry of Agriculture
  Fisheries & Food,
Tolcarne Drive,
Pinner,
Middlesex HA5 2DT.

British Rabbit Council,
Purefoy House,
7 Kirkgate,
Newark, Nottinghamshire.

Commercial Rabbit
  Association,
Tyning House,
Shurdington,
Cheltenham,
Glos. GL51 5XF.

Health Education Council,
78 New Oxford Street,
London, WC1A 1AH
for free leaflet—*Your Guide
  to Food Hygiene (General)
  Regulation 1970*

Tasseltips Angoras,
Wood Farm,
Ubbeston,
Halesworth,
Suffolk IP19 0EU
for information on
breeding stock and
production of fibre,
including spinning.

Equipment
George H. Eltex Ltd.,
Dept. 47,
Eltex Works,
Worcester.

R. H. & B. Moncaster,
West End Villa,
Ludford,
Lincoln, LN3 6AJ.

Breeding Stock and Equipment
Hylyne Rabbits Ltd.,
Marston, Northwich,
Cheshire, CW9 6ER

Commercial Rabbit Equipment
J. Davies,
Grange Cottage,
Balderton,
Newark,
Notts.

Appendix II

Publications

Ministry of Agriculture Fisheries & Food Advisory Leaflets obtainable from H. M. Stationery Office agents in principal towns:

AL 544 General Management & Housing
   556 Breeding Principles and Systems
   557 Economics and a Record System
   562 Feeding of Meat Rabbits
   565 Breeds of Rabbits

British Poisonous Plants, Bulletin No. 161

Fur & Feather Fortnightly publication

Commercial Rabbit Monthly periodical

The Domestic Rabbit by J. C. Sandford, published by Crosby Lockwood & Son Ltd.

Green Foods for Rabbits and Cavies by I. R. Bell, published by Watmoughs Ltd., Idle, Bradford.

Smallholder Monthly magazine, Charter Magazines Ltd., Bank Chambers, Downham Market, Norfolk PE38 9BU.

Index